Everycat

A Complete Book of Cat Care

ERIC ALLAN LYNDA BONNING

Melbourne

OXFORD UNIVERSITY PRESS

Oxford Auckland New York

OXFORD UNIVERSITY PRESS AUSTRALIA

Oxford   New York
Athens   Auckland   Bangkok   Bogota   Bombay
Buenos Aires   Calcutta   Cape Town   Dar es Salaam
Delhi   Florence   Hong Kong   Istanbul   Karachi
Kuala Lumpur   Madras   Madrid   Melbourne
Mexico City   Nairobi   Paris   Port Moresby
Singapore   Taipei   Tokyo   Toronto   Warsaw
and associated companies in
Berlin   Ibadan

OXFORD is a trade mark of Oxford University Press

National Library of Australia
Cataloguing-in-Publication data:

Allan, Eric
Every cat: a complete book of cat care

3rd ed.
Includes index
ISBN 0 19 554004 2.

1. Cats. 2. Cats - Behaviour. 3. Cats - Diseases.
I. Bonning, Lynda. II. Title.

636.8083

Edited by Cathryn Game
Illustrated by Christopher Seater
Indexed by Julia Allan
Text designed by Cath Lindsey
Cover design by Anitra Blackford
Cover photograph from Horizon Photo Library
Typeset by Desktop Concepts P/L, Melbourne
Printed through Bookpac Production Services, Singapore
Published by Oxford University Press,
253 Normanby Road, South Melbourne, Australia

Contents

Acknowledgments

Thanks to Dr J. Rowan Blogg, Diplomate of the American College of Veterinary Ophthalmologists, for writing the chapter on the eye. We are also extremely grateful for the generous help, freely given, of many other people.

Dr Peter Cullen gave invaluable assistance on the subject of reproduction, and we are especially indebted to him. Thanks to Dr Ulrike Wurth, BVSc, DipAc (IVAS certified) for her help in compiling the section on acupuncture. Thanks to Dr Carolyn Ashton, BVSc, for help with the sections on essential oils and flower essences; she has used the latter extensively with cats. The section on herbal remedies was compiled by Rebecca Palmer, DMV.

Thanks also to Dr Jack Arundal, Dr James Greenwood, Uncle Ben's of Australia, Mr and Mrs J. Chitty, Gayle McPhee, Dr Virginia Studdert, Dr Sonya Bettonay and in particular to Pam and Warren Bonning for their support. Lesley Abbott not only rapidly and accurately typed the manuscript but was also unfailingly cooperative and tolerant. Thanks also to Kingsley Abbott for cheerfully facing the drudgery of checking it all.

Introduction

Everycat is for all cat owners. It contains the advice your vet would give you if only there was enough time, but it is also all about your cat. We hope it will help you to enjoy your cat to the full.

In this third edition we have acknowledged the growing interest in alternatives to traditional veterinary treatment in our chapter on natural remedies and healing. Acupuncture has now become firmly established as a treatment option, and it could be that other 'natural' therapies, such as aromatherapy, flower essences and naturopathy, will also become more acceptable to mainstream practice.

As well as updating and revising, we have also included a section for owners to help deal with the loss of a pet and the grief that surrounds this experience.

Every effort has been made to give accurate and reliable information without resorting to technical jargon. Concerned owners require information from their veterinarians so that informed decisions about their pet's welfare can be made. A lot of questions are asked of us in our daily consultations, and we have attempted to answer them all here. We know it is difficult to take in a lot of new information while standing in a veterinarian's office, feeling anxious and perhaps a little distracted. With *Everycat* you can relax at home and take your time, 'digesting' the answers to your queries.

Cat owners often ask how a vet can diagnose a cat's problem without being able to question the patient. The answer lies in careful observation and recognition of abnormalities and signs of illness. This book will help you to do the same. Sometimes all you need is general advice or credible information. At others a crisis might arise, for example, if you suspect poisoning. The correct action on your part could save your cat's life. Early recognition of disease can prevent unnecessary discomfort.

Your cat cannot take itself to the vet. Its welfare is in your hands.

Enjoy your cat.

1 LIVING WITH A CAT

Kittens are extraordinarily appealing little bundles of fun. Unfortunately, a large number of people impulsively acquire a kitten without considering what they are taking on. Before you get a cat, you must be sure you are willing to house, feed and maintain it for the next 10–15 years. The cat will need regular meals. You might have to clean litter trays, groom the cat, and provide some exercise and entertainment. The costs of vaccination and neutering will have to be met, and the cat could have additional occasional problems, such as fleas, worms and sickness.

Too many cats are abandoned or destroyed because people haven't thought the problems through. In almost every major city in the world, thousands of cats are destroyed every week by welfare societies. This is an appalling situation, but you can do your part by being a responsible owner.

CHOOSING THE CAT FOR YOU

Here are a few points to ponder while you are mulling over your choice.

Type

Longhair or shorthair? The longhairs can look magnificent, but they do require *daily* grooming. They also tend to shed more hair on furniture and carpets, and are less suitable than shorthairs for hot climates.

Breed

There is a lot less variation between the characteristics of the cat breeds than there is between dog breeds. Nevertheless, there are some fairly well-defined traits, although it should also be stressed that every cat is an individual. All these comments are generalisations.

Pedigree or non-pedigree?

Pedigree cats are more expensive, especially if sold for breeding and the showring. You could be offered a pedigree cat for a relatively low fee if it is unsuitable for showing due to some fault in coat, colour or conformation. This does not necessarily mean this particular cat will be unhealthy or unsuitable as a pet, but before you commit yourself to a sale, ask carefully what the faults are, and get your vet's comments and advice.

Male cats make much better pets if they are neutered

Sex

Unless you are a keen breeder, you should have your cat neutered. Once they have been neutered, there is little difference between the sexes. If you do not want to have your cat neutered, then a female is much easier to keep than a male. An 'entire' male (that is, not neutered) is usually dominated by his sex drive. They can be very smelly and aggressive, especially towards other male cats. We strongly recommend that you have your cat neutered.

Table 1: Breeds of cat and their characteristics

Breed	Temperament	Voice	Comment
Shorthaired			
Siamese	A sociable cat, very outgoing personality. Can become strongly attached to owners. Very demanding of both attention and affection. Enjoys sitting on laps. Intelligent, but often highly strung and tendency to be neurotic. Good with children if brought up with them.	Very loud voice — a penetrating distinct meow, which they tend to use excessively. Can be hard to take (especially when queen is on heat).	Indiscriminate breeding has produced some faults in the breed, e.g. crossed eyes, skeletal disease, kinked tails and abnormal temperaments. Observe parents before buying a kitten.
Burmese	Intelligent, easygoing and adaptable. Affectionate and attention-seeking. Good with children if brought up with them.	Much less vocally demanding than the Siamese.	Increasingly popular breed.
Abyssinian	Gentle and affectionate, often shy and reserved. Apprehensive with strangers and can be nervous with children.	Quiet voice.	Becoming more popular.
Rex	Intelligent, inquisitive, extrovert. Often highly strung. Tendency toward sulky moods.	Not very noisy.	Relatively high incidence of slipping kneecaps in the breed. Don't shed hair like other cats, might be suitable in a household where someone is allergic to cat hair.
Longhaired			
Persian	Mainly placid, gentle temperament. Often reserved and shy. Not particularly demanding of affection or attention. Some have fiery tempers.	A melodious voice compared to Siamese. Don't vocalise often.	Usually adjust well to strange environments. Coats need to be groomed daily.

Table 1: Breeds of cat and their characteristics (*cont*)

Breed	Temperament	Voice	Comment
Himalayan	Gentle temperament with an outgoing personality. Not as demanding as Siamese and generally more affectionate than Persian.	Not very noisy.	A breed that is becoming more popular. Cat needs to be groomed daily.
Birman	Placid, friendly nature. Affectionate, but can be demanding.	Not very vocal until they want something.	Relatively uncommon breed, but growing in popularity. Coat needs daily grooming.
Angora	Gentle cat that can be highly strung and nervous.	Not a very vocal breed.	Loves water and swimming. Needs daily grooming.

Note: These comments are only meant as a guide—there will be exceptions to these guidelines. Many other breeds that have not been mentioned are available.

The age to buy

The kitten is weaned from its mother at about 4–5 weeks of age. Around this time, the kitten will adapt fairly easily to a change in environment, and could form a fairly strong bond of attachment to you. Six weeks of age seems to be the optimum time to acquire a kitten. However, there might be situations in which an older cat is more suitable. For example, elderly people might find a kitten too much of a handful, or a working couple might be unable to feed and tend to a youngster adequately.

Rearing a young kitten can be very rewarding. You can help to shape its personality. If you have children, it is best to get a young kitten as it will grow up in the rough and tumble and learn to cope, whereas an adult cat could become distressed or frightened with boisterous behaviour.

WHERE TO BUY A CAT

Private homes

Private homes are usually the best source. The kittens will probably have been handled from early in life, which makes them much more socially adaptable. There is less risk of the kitten contracting infectious diseases (such as cat flu) and parasites than there is in breeding establishments or welfare homes. You can ask about the parents' personalities, and it will give you some guide as to what to expect from their progeny.

Pet shops

Pet shops can be good, but be careful. Be sure the kittens are kept under clean, hygienic conditions, otherwise you could be buying trouble. Many pet shops are excellent, but others are a source of feline enteritis, cat flu, ringworm, mange, fleas and other conditions.

Humane or cat welfare organisations

These groups do a great service to cats. They are usually staffed by genuinely concerned cat lovers. But beware! Kittens from *some* of these homes can be sick or incubating diseases. Sometimes you could be offered kittens of wild or feral cats, which can be difficult to tame. They could be unsatisfactory as pets. If you choose a cat from one of these organisations, be very careful in your choice. Don't let your heart rule your head.

Your vet

Your vet might have clients who are looking for good homes for cats or kittens.

Pedigreed animals

Pedigreed animals can be obtained through the various cat fanciers' organisations. Telephone the secretary of the appropriate breed society for information and a list of breeders who have kittens for sale.

THE PICK OF THE LITTER

Given a bunch of playful kittens to choose from, how do you pick the one most likely to suit you? First, be sure the kittens are healthy. Here is a list of points to check:

- Should be lively, active and well nourished.
- Feel the kitten—don't just look. The ribs should not protrude, nor should the kitten have a pot-belly.
- Coat: soft, with a light sheen, not dry or harsh.
- Eyes: clear and no discharge.
- Ears: clean and no discharge or offensive smell.
- Mouth: should have all the milk teeth.
- Legs: straight, not bowed.
- Should be properly weaned, and not still sucking.
- Look for evidence of diarrhoea. This matts the hair around the anus and might stain the hocks.
- Ask what worming has been done and what vaccinations (if any) the kitten has had. A vaccination certificate should be available.
- Should be used to being handled, otherwise it might be difficult to handle when older, and is especially likely to be wary of strangers.

The kitten for you

If possible, see the whole litter together, look for a kitten that is alert and playful, and which responds to your approach with interest, not fear. This sort of kitten is likely to make a good pet.

The kitten that approaches you first is liable to have a dominant personality. Select it only if you want a strong-willed cat that is likely to be independent. The kitten that sits back or shies away is likely to be sensitive, and will need patience and gentleness. Do not choose this kitten unless you are prepared to spend time gaining the cat's confidence. It will not be suitable for young children or for a person who is intending to move around a lot.

It is tempting to feel sorry for the runt of the litter. Don't rush in without considering what you could be taking on. This kitten will almost certainly have some problems and might be liable to sickness. You will probably have the cat for many years—are you prepared to look after it? Some people gain great satisfaction and pleasure from rearing such a kitten, but it takes a special type of owner.

Avoid aggressive kittens. They almost invariably grow to be aggressive adults.

It is usually possible to make your purchase conditional on a satisfactory report from your vet. We recommend a veterinary examination, especially if purchasing a pedigreed cat. If the kitten has a pedigree, take it with you to your vet. Look carefully for evidence of inbreeding (your vet will help you here). The pedigree should be complete and the kitten registered with the appropriate breed society.

Should you get two kittens?

You might consider getting two kittens to keep each other company, especially if you are away from home a lot. This is usually not necessary, as most cats are very independent and perfectly happy to be the sole resident of your home. If you want to have two cats, it is best to start them off together rather than introduce another kitten later, as this second kitten could be rejected or resented. The best combination seems to be a male and a female. Two females usually get on well together, but two males are less predictable. Behavioural pressures of dominance and territorial rights might come between them, even if both are neutered.

What will you need for the new arrival?

- Food and water bowl.
- Sleeping box or basket.
- Litter tray and litter.
- Cat food.
- Perhaps a scratching post.
- A cat collar.

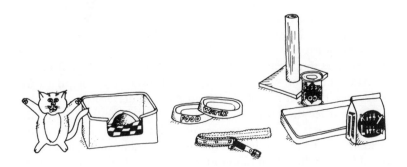

In some areas it is mandatory that cats wear a collar with a registration tag. Not everyone agrees that a cat should wear a collar. We feel they should. If the cat is lost or injured you have a good chance of recovering it if you have an identification tag on the collar. Without a collar, the chances are very poor. A cat collar is special. It has a soft, felt lining and a piece of elastic sewn in so that, if the cat is caught by the collar, it will expand to slip over the head. Cats should be introduced to collars when young. It might be difficult to get an adult to start wearing one.

THE FIRST DAY

If possible, collect the kitten on a weekend or a holiday so that you have time to help the new arrival settle in. Shut all the doors and windows. Select where you want the kitten to eat and a different spot for the litter tray. Keep these positions constant so that the kitten can develop a routine. Put the kitten down on its bed. Then step back and allow it to move quietly about and explore. Don't fuss over or overexcite the kitten. Give it time. You will be able to tell when the kitten has relaxed as it will sit down and begin to groom itself. At this stage offer some food. (And have a cup of coffee yourself. You probably need it!)

For the first few days, feed the kitten the same diet that the breeders had been feeding. Only gradually change to your own selection. Beware especially of giving milk as it might cause diarrhoea.

The first night can be a trauma. Give the kitten a source of warmth, such as a hot water bottle wrapped in an old jumper. A soft toy that the kitten can snuggle against might help. Some kittens are soothed by a loud ticking alarm clock. One theory is that the ticking substitutes for the mother's heartbeat. Perhaps it does, or perhaps it just provides something regular and reliable to break the solitude.

After meals, or when the kitten first awakes, put it on to its toilet area. Praise it if it obligingly urinates or defaecates.

Do not let the kitten outside until it has become used to its feeding place. Once that pattern is established it will return for food. It is dangerous to let the kitten out without supervision. You should *not* let the kitten out at night as it is likely to be harmed by prowling adult cats, and there is also a high risk of it being run over on the road.

Cats like to sleep above floor level. As your kitten grows, you could put its basket up on to a suitable shelf in an attempt to avoid it making its own choice of chairs or other furniture. It is not easy to bend a cat's will, and most will make their own decision as to where they are going to sleep. Some cats will change their preferred sleeping area every so often, but most are consistent, although they have several resting or napping areas.

Meeting other pets

You have probably seen pictures of cats living happily with mice or birds or other little animals. Be warned.

These are exceptions to the rule. The cat is a hunter, with strong instincts bred in over thousands of years. They do not usually get along with small mammals such as guinea pigs, hamsters, rabbits or mice. Nor with birds or fish. If you have other such pets, you must provide them with a secure hutch or cage and don't allow the cat to interfere with them. The tops of fish bowls should be covered.

If you have a dog, keep the two apart on the first day. Introduce them under supervision, preferably with a leash on the dog. Be ready to pull the dog away. Most dogs will accept a young kitten. They might even grow to be close companions. Initially, expect a few hisses and the occasional slap with a paw. It you have a puppy, be careful it is not scratched in the eye.

Always feed the dog and the cat in their own bowls, preferably in separate areas. The cat can be fed at a height on a bench or table-top, so that the dog does not get at its food.

Health

Cats can be vaccinated against feline infectious enteritis (panleukopaenia), the feline respiratory diseases (cat flu), various other diseases, and in some countries rabies. Temporary vaccinations can be given from 6 weeks of age and 'permanent' vaccinations from 12 weeks. Read

VACCINATION

the chapter on infectious diseases and see your own vet for recommended dose regimes.

You should worm your kitten when you get it, and then every 2–4 weeks. See the section on internal parasites in chapter 14, 'The Gut'.

If your kitten has fleas you should try to remove them at once before too many eggs are laid. See the section on flea control in chapter 13, 'Skin and Coat'.

TRAINING

Choose a name for your kitten as early as possible, then repeat it whenever you are stroking the kitten. Call the name when the kitten is walking towards you, when you are putting the food down and on greeting it first thing in the morning.

The kitten will soon associate the name with itself.

Use simple, single words. A firm tone for commands is essential. Do not try for too much at once. Try these few for a start:

NO! When the kitten is removed from some undesirable activity, such as urinating on the carpet or demolishing a pot plant.

DOWN! As you put the kitten down off your lap or from a table or chair.

OUT! As you put the kitten out the door, especially if this is to go to the toilet area.

It is useless to use phrases such as 'you are a naughty boy.' A simple NO is much more effective.

Reward, not punishment, is the best teacher. Reward the kitten for good behaviour with praise and affection, and perhaps with a treat or titbit. Never feed a cat after it has misbehaved. Wait for at least 20 minutes. Otherwise, the cat might interpret the food as a reward associated with the offensive activity.

Habits that are cute in a kitten can be a real problem when the cat grows up. Do not let the kitten sleep on your bed or get away with scratching the furniture, crawling up your trouser leg or biting your hand.

If you must punish, be aware that it is easy to establish distrust in the cat. However, if the cat behaves aggressively or dominantly, you should establish *your* dominance immediately, firmly and consistently. Use a similar sort of body language to the methods the kitten's mother would use. Grasp the offender by the scruff, firmly saying NO! *Or* use a rolled-up newspaper to slap the kitten on the snout. The noise and the domination of the act are enough. You should not give the kitten more than a light tap. Never physically hurt the kitten.

For constant misbehaviour other than aggression, do not use physical punishment.Instead, use 'aversion therapy.' The idea of aversion therapy is to get the cat to associate the unwelcome activity with something unpleasant. If possible, the cat should not associate you with the unpleasantness, as this can lead to a lack of trust. An ideal tool is a water pistol, or you could throw a rolled up ball of paper at the cat or throw a bunch of keys near the cat to startle it. Every time you see the cat attempting the undesired activity, such as scratching the furniture, give a quick squirt, but try not to let the cat see you doing the squirting.

In some cases, you can 'set up' the cat. For example, if the cat has developed the unwelcome habit of sleeping in the clothes basket, you could put in a balloon filled with water almost to bursting point, then cover it with some old clothes. After a couple of wet surprises the cat is very unlikely to return. If the cat is pulling clothes from a drying rack, then put a water balloon inside a tempting sock.

Toilet training

Most kittens have already been toilet trained by their mother, or will automatically seek out somewhere to bury their excreta. If the kitten is not already trained, it is usually easy to do so. Put the kitten into the litter box or toilet area immediately after feeding or on waking. Hold the front paws and make digging actions, showing it

how to scratch amongst the litter. (The kitten will use its *back* paws, but they usually resent you pulling at them.) The kitten will generally catch on quickly.

The litter should be cleaned daily. Many cats will not use soiled litter and might therefore soil elsewhere. If you find your cat will not use litter, try sand or soil. If possible, establish an outside toilet area as well.

Praise and stroke the cat to reward it for correct toilet habits. If you actually catch it in the act of soiling the floor, use harsh voice tones or the aversion technique. Do not use physical punishment. Definitely do not rub the kitten's nose in the mess. This is likely to cause mistrust and make the problem worse since it stresses the cat.

Chapter 5 on behaviour discusses how to deal with inappropriate urinating as well as other subjects such as furniture scratching and killing birds.

INDOOR CATS

Cats are perfectly able to live long and contented lives without venturing outside. You need not feel guilty about denying your cat an outside roaming area. You will need to make some concessions if you want an indoor cat, but for many owners the advantages of keeping the cat in far outweigh the drawbacks.

Good reasons for staying in

In many situations, such as in high-rise buildings, inner-city areas and environmentally sensitive zones, it is not possible to let cats out to roam. In others, it is advisable not to, and more people are simply choosing to keep their cats inside the home.

The law

Legal restrictions detailing whether and when cats are allowed to wander are in force in an increasing number of areas. Animals found in breach of these regulations are impounded, and owners face a fine. Contact your local authority or vet to find out what restrictions apply to your area.

Safety

A cat is relatively safe inside. An outside cat faces two very common threats: fight injuries and motor vehicle accidents. Cat fights are very common as it is in the cat's nature to dispute territory. Bite wounds produce potentially serious infections, not only in the form of bacterial abscesses but also by spreading such diseases as FIV and feline leukaemia.

Good public relations

Roaming cats tend to be very irritating to non-cat-loving neighbours, particularly at night time. Everyone appreciates responsible pet ownership.

Staying in

Keeping your cat indoors permanently is best achieved by *never* letting it outside from kittenhood onwards. It is far more difficult to curtail an adult cat that has become used to free movement outside, but it is certainly possible, and eventually the cat will settle down to a contented indoor existence.

Cats that are never let outside ultimately make no attempts to leave even when an opportunity exists, such as when doors or windows are left open. If they do get outside they are likely to return rapidly to where they feel safe and familiar.

Keeping them happy requires environmental enrichment.

Environmental enrichment

For cats kept indoors it is vitally important that their environment offers them plenty of enrichment. Carpeted cat 'trees' with shelves and cubbies are great. Cats like to have access to more than one vertical level, so shelves up a wall in a step pattern, or furniture arranged strategically step-wise to a high platform, are well appreciated. Pet electric blankets in sleeping areas can be a good idea, particularly if the cat is left in a cold house for much of the day. Cardboard boxes make good play items, and furry toy mice to bat around the room are also good therapy. Items dangled from wool or string are entertaining but should only be used under supervision in case they become entangled. Cats like to chase fast-moving objects, and a red laser spot of light can be moved around the room, up walls and along shelves, providing great exercise for the cat and great amusement for the owner!

Another way of enriching the environment is to provide an outside fenced-in area with access from inside through a window or cat door, or having an independent outside aviary-type area, to which the cat can be carried and placed inside. They do like to feel the wind in their ears and chase the odd leaf as well as bask in the sun in these outside enclosures. Prefabricated outdoor modular cat enclosures can be obtained. They can be set up to include trees and bushes in a configuration that suits your backyard. Balcony areas can be tastefully enclosed for this purpose, too, if space is not available.

Another form of environmental enrichment for the confined cat is to provide another cat for a companion. Introducing two adult cats can be a challenge, but with perseverance, and maybe some veterinary intervention, it is usually successful and rewarding. The easiest way is to get two kittens at the same time, or within a few weeks of each other, so that they grow up together. The cats usually spend many hours having mock fights, lying in ambush for each other and ultimately settling down to using one another as a pillow.

Pot plants can be grown for your cat in the house. Catnip, cat-mint and catgrass are safe for your cat to chew, smell and rub against. Try leaving celery tops standing up in a corner for the cat to chew and rub against.

The cat litter dilemma

One of the most common, and most strongly voiced, objections to indoor cats is the aversion of many owners to having kitty litter around the house. Cat urine and faeces can become extremely objectionable, but if you manage this potential problem well it can be completely negated. Enclosed litter trays are available. They are very effective in confining both the odours and scattered litter. Alternatively, the litter tray can be placed in a cupboard and a cat access hole cut in the door (with a flap if you like). This greatly reduces the intrusiveness of cat litter, helps to confine the mess and odour, and gives cats the privacy that many prefer.

There are many different varieties of litter. Some cats prefer particular types, and the same goes for their owners. There is a great variation in weight, efficiency of absorption, odour controlling qualities, cost, etc. Some owners use sand or dirt from their garden, but this can be a source of toxoplasmosis (see p. 140). Some of the substances available include limestone gravel, untreated sawdust, pelleted grass, or recycled products such as blotter-like pellets made from used paper products like telephone directories or newspaper. Biodegradable products are definitely to be encouraged.

Diet also plays an important role in minimising the smell from the litter area. Some types of food make the cat's faeces more pungent than others. Experiment with different brands and formulations of reputable cat foods to find out which one is the most suitable for your cat.

EXERCISE

Cats need exercise. They are athletic creatures. Constant confinement without an outlet for exercise and play can lead to a dull, apathetic cat or to the development of destructive behaviour. Bored cats might damage plants or soft furnishings or might become neurotic.

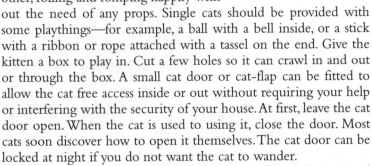

Two kittens will exercise each other, rolling and romping happily without the need of any props. Single cats should be provided with some playthings—for example, a ball with a bell inside, or a stick with a ribbon or rope attached with a tassel on the end. Give the kitten a box to play in. Cut a few holes so it can crawl in and out or through the box. A small cat door or cat-flap can be fitted to allow the cat free access inside or out without requiring your help or interfering with the security of your house. At first, leave the cat door open. When the cat is used to using it, close the door. Most cats soon discover how to open it themselves. The cat door can be locked at night if you do not want the cat to wander.

Some owners are able to train their cat to walk on a harness and lead, and exercise them that way.

TRAVELLING

If the cat is not used to travelling in a car or other vehicle, you must confine it in a strong, secure container. Specially designed cat carry baskets or bags are available. You can make do with a box, but it

must be strong and capable of being securely fastened. Cardboard boxes are usually unsuitable as the cat is likely to urinate, and a wet box loses its strength.

A zip-fastening bag will do for things like a trip to the vet. The cat will not smother. If the journey is a long one, it will be necessary to provide more room and better airflow than a zip-up bag allows. Don't make the mistake of leaving the zip partly undone. Cats can squeeze out through remarkably small gaps.

Withhold all food and water for several hours before the journey. Unless you are travelling for more than 12 hours it is not necessary to provide food. If it is hot, be certain the box is well ventilated and the cat has access to water.

Some cats travel well. Some don't. If your cat is a nervous traveller it might be advisable to give a tranquilliser first. (Do not experiment with drugs or dose rates. Seek the correct advice from the vet.)

Do not be tempted to travel with your cat roaming free in the car or sitting on your lap. A frightened or hysterical cat is extremely dangerous, especially when trapped inside a moving vehicle.

You can help the cat to become used to travelling without trauma by introducing it to the experience gradually. Sit with the cat in a stationary car, with and without the motor running. Feed a few treats. Indulge in a little play session, then try a few short drives—up and down the driveway first, then around the block.

Travel by air, rail and sea

Organise your cat's transport well in advance if possible. All transport companies have specific requirements, and they will usually send you a list of them, plus some guidelines to follow.

If you are travelling abroad there might be vaccination and other regulations to comply with. Some countries have strict quarantine requirements. Check with your Department of Agriculture or Department of Health. Your vet will probably know who to contact.

Boarding your cat

The vast majority of cats will settle perfectly happily into a boarding cattery, contrary to the expectations of the vast majority of cat owners. It usually takes one or two days for the cat to become familiar with the new surroundings and to realise it is safe and secure and that food is available. After that, they generally seem content.

It is worth taking the time to select a good cattery. Ask friends for their recommendations. Here are a few guidelines you might bear in mind when making your choice:

- Look for clean, hygienic conditions. The smell inside the cattery will give you some guide.

- There should be no opportunity for direct 'nose to nose' contact between cats. There should be solid partitioning or a space between the cages.
- Cats should not be admitted without a current vaccination certificate.
- Cats do not need a huge area, but they should have enough room for separate eating, sleeping and toilet areas.
- Ask what the cat will be fed. Does the cattery cater to individuals which are choosy or require a special diet?
- Ask what the proprietor would do if your cat fell ill.

Advance bookings are usually necessary, especially on public holidays or in summer. Plan ahead, or you might have to settle for a second-rate establishment.

2 FIRST AID

GIVING MEDICINE

Getting a cat to take the medicine it needs but probably doesn't want can be a problem unless you use the correct techniques. Get yourself organised first, with the tablet ready and a blanket handy. It is easier to put the cat on a table than to struggle on the floor. If the cat is likely to struggle and scratch, envelop it tightly in a blanket first, leaving only the head exposed.

To give a tablet, try the following method:

- Hold the cat's head in your left hand, with your thumb on one corner of the jaw and forefinger on the other, so that your hand spans the cat's head just behind the eyeline. The ears should be under the palm of your hand. By holding the head in this manner you can get a firm grip without hurting the cat.
- Do *not* grip the cat around the neck. The cat is liable to panic and you could be severely scratched or bitten.
- Tip the cat's head back.
- With your right hand, open the cat's mouth by putting the nail (only) of your forefinger on the teeth of the cat's lower jaw and pull down. The mouth will usually open easily.

- The pill must be placed right at the back of the cat's mouth, over the hump of the tongue. Throw the pill to the back of the mouth and quickly push it out of sight. You could use your finger, but a pencil or similar might be safer. Keep your finger in the *center* of the mouth—do not come in over the side teeth, or you could easily be bitten.
- If the cat struggles or claws, envelop it in a large towel or blanket, leaving only the head exposed.

Other ways of giving medicine

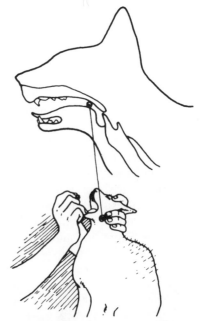

xThe tablet must be pushed right to the back of the throat, over the hump of the tongue

If you have trouble actually physically giving a tablet, here are a few ideas on how to give the medicine in other ways.

It is not sufficient simply to hide the tablet from view. Cats detect these unwelcome additions to their food mainly by smell. For example, if you had fifty pieces of meat and you picked up one piece, then put it down again, the chances are the cat would leave that particular piece. It will at least examine it closely before consuming it, even though it contained no drugs. It is your odour that the cat detects. Any unusual smell will immediately alert the cat. So if you handle a single piece of meat to insert a tablet, the cat will usually detect it.

If the tablet can be crushed (some must not be crushed: they might have a protective coating to disguise a bitter taste or to protect them from stomach acids) then you might succeed in disguising it if you mix it with a strong-smelling food. First, powder the tablet. It is not enough just to break it into a few pieces. Then mix it thoroughly with a food you know your cat likes, and which has a strong odour, for example fish or cheese. Let it sit for about 20 minutes before feeding it to the cat.

If the tablet is not suitable for crushing, cut a deep hole in a piece of meat or cheese, and push the tablet in. Do not simply wrap the food around the tablet. If you have had to handle the doctored piece of food, handle all the others as well before offering the food to the cat. A gravy poured over the lot might help.

If these methods fail, crush the tablet and mix it with a little yeast extract or honey, and smear the mixture on to the cat's forepaw. The cat's fastidious nature will usually drive it to lick the paw clean.

If you have no success with tablets, ask your vet if the required medicine is available in liquid form. Liquids are generally easier to give than tablets (if only a small volume is required). To administer a syrup, paste or liquid, simply hold the cat's head as described above, tip it back slightly, and introduce the nozzle of the loaded dropper or

syringe into the mouth just behind the canine tooth. There is a gap in the teeth here, so there is no need to prise the cat's jaw apart.

HANDLING AN INJURED CAT

Be cautious when handling any injured animal. A cat that is frightened or in pain can be dangerous. Be gentle and patient. Do not take risks if the cat is uncooperative.

The cooperative cat

If the cat is quiet and tranquil your main aims are to minimise further damage and to use handling techniques that minimise pain and discomfort.

First: Before attempting to lift the cat, reassure it by speaking in a calm, level voice. Stroke the cat softly, with a slow soothing action.

Then: Pick the cat up using one of these techniques: (a) hand under chest and rump; or (b) scruff of neck and rump.

The uncooperative cat

Beware of the frightened cat. Teeth and claws can inflict severe damage. Even your own normally placid cat can be unpredictable when frightened.

Warning signs: If the cat watches you with wide open (dilated) pupils, has the ears flattened and hisses at your approach, then *do not* attempt to pick it up.

If possible, leave the cat alone until it has calmed. Take your time. Stay at a safe distance. Reassure the cat by talking quietly. Do not stare into the cat's eyes as this has an unsettling effect. In many cases, the cat will gradually calm and will then be able to be picked up.

If urgent attention is necessary or if the cat is in a dangerous position, such as lying on a roadway, or if the cat's attitude is unlikely to improve, the following technique may be used:

- Get a large blanket, towel or coat.
- Drop it over the cat, enveloping it.
- Scoop the entire bundle up, tucking the edges firmly into the bundle. All four limbs and head must be included. Don't worry, the cat will not smother.
- Put the entire bundle—blanket, cat and all—into a secure box, or you could carry the cat directly to the vet.

If first aid treatment of a limb or the head is essential, expose *only* that part, keeping the blanket firmly wrapped around the rest of the cat.

ABSCESS

An *abscess* is a localised collection of pus. A 'wall' of thick, fibrous tissue encompasses this pus. Most abscesses form as a result of puncture wounds inflicted during cat fights. Other possible causes include a reaction to a foreign body, such as a grass seed or wood splinter. Infection can develop within a deep cut or abrasion or even a surgical wound. Abscesses sometimes flare due to some chronic irritation, such as an ingrowing toenail, or a tumour. The abscess might rupture spontaneously, discharging the thick, yellow or brown foul-smelling liquid pus. Or the abscess might have to be opened (or 'lanced') by you or your vet.

Abscesses usually take 3–5 days to form after the initiating wound. By this time they can be seen or felt as soft or fluctuating, painful swellings under the skin. The most common sites of abscesses in cats are on the side of the face (especially so in tom cats), or around the base of the tail. Because of the cat's thick coat, the full size of the infected area might not be readily apparent, especially for the first 2–3 days after the initiating wound. Usually, all you see is a swollen, tense and discoloured area of skin.

If the abscess is large (that is, more than a centimetre in diameter) or if the cat is in pain or is lethargic or off its food, then veterinary attention is advisable.

Should the abscess be opened?

If the abscess has not spontaneously burst, you might be able to bring it to a 'head' by gently bathing with a mild solution of salt or bicarbonate of soda. If it has not ruptured within 24 hours, it might have to be lanced. This is best done by your vet, but if necessary you could do it yourself using a very sharp, sterilised knife blade or a razor blade. The cut is made in the lowest part of the abscess. Cut into the tense skin covering the swollen mass. The aim is to allow all the pus to drain away.

After lancing, the abscess cavity is flushed with a mild antiseptic solution (such as 2% hydrogen peroxide). Antibiotics may be required to eliminate bacterial infection completely and so prevent the abscess re-forming. Keep the drainage hole open for at least 24 hours and preferably 48 hours. Gently bathe away any scab that forms. The more discharge that escapes, the better.

If the abscess has already burst, what is the next step?

Try to keep the abscess draining. Aim to clean out as much of the discharge as possible. Most will drain out, but there are usually residues that could prevent resolution of the infection or even lead to the abscess re-forming.

If the abscess has burst, try to massage all the pus out gently — if the cat will let you

Usually the cat will lick away the pus. This might seem nauseating to us, but it does not seem to do the cat any harm. If the cat cannot reach the abscess to clean it, then clean it by gently bathing or flushing with saline, clean water or a very mild antiseptic solution.

When to call the vet

- Cat is lethargic, off food or in pain.
- The abscess is extensive.
- Abscess ruptures but is not clearing up, or has re-formed.

If you *know* your cat has been bitten it is best to go to your vet straight away. Penetrating bite wounds are almost always infected. It is better to get immediate treatment than to wait for and abscess to develop. *Beware:* What might appear to be a small abscess could be only a part of a more extensive problem. Don't delay your visit to the vet if your cat is clearly ill.

BLEEDING

The primary first aid aim is to minimise blood loss. Fortunately, cats usually don't bleed much, even from quite severe wounds. However, if a major blood vessel is damaged, the cat could lose a lot of blood in a short time.

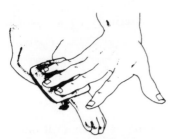

To stop bleeding: apply pressure on a pad placed over the bleeding area

Beware: The cat will resent your attention. Be cautious when dealing with an injured cat.

The simplest way to slow or stop bleeding is to apply pressure directly over the site, if this is possible:

- Get bandages. Gauze is ideal. In an emergency a handkerchief, tie or strips of cloth will suffice.
- If possible, first coat a gauze pad with a little white petroleum jelly. This prevents it sticking to the wound and pulling the clot off later.
- Apply this pad to the wound.
- Press down on the pad, applying pressure with your fingers. Don't press too hard or the cat will resent it.
- Wrap a bandage or cloth strip over the pad. The bandage should be firm not tight.
- If blood seeps through, apply another bandage *over the first.* Do *not* remove the lowest pad or you will disturb any clot that is forming.

Tourniquets

Tourniquets can be used if there is severe bleeding of a leg or tail. Tourniquets should only be used as a last resort as they can cause further damage. Many cats will not tolerate them. Tourniquets must be loosened for ½–1 minute in every 10 or serious tissue damage could occur due to lack of oxygen. To apply a tourniquet, use a broad belt, tie or piece of cloth. Apply it well above the bleeding area. Insert a piece of wood or a pen into the circle of cloth and twist it tight.

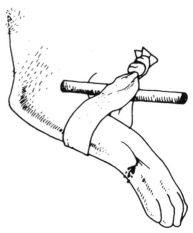

Tourniquets can be life saving, but are dangerous

When to call the vet

After any episode of severe bleeding, veterinary advice should be sought.

BITES

Cat bites

Cat fights are common, especially in spring or when a cat moves into a new territory. The two most frequently bitten areas are around the face and neck, and around the base of the tail.

A common complication of a cat bite is infection. The cat's canine teeth make deep puncture wounds. Bacteria from the cat's mouth and from the victim's skin are virtually injected into the wound. It can be difficult to locate the wound as the small punctures are concealed by the coat. Bleeding from the wound site is usually minimal.

Assuming you do find the wound, and the cat is cooperative, you should first gently clip away the surrounding hair. Then clean the area with a dilute antiseptic such as 2% hydrogen peroxide. Finally, paint it with an antiseptic. A 'tamed' iodine preparation (i.e. one that doesn't sting) is quite effective.

In many cases you will be either unaware of the initial bite or will be unable to find the wound until 3–4 days after the event. By this stage, the bacteria will have established themselves and multi-plied. The affected area becomes red, swollen and very tender. By the fourth or fifth day an abscess might have developed. Antibiotics are usually indicated if such an infection has developed.

If your cat has been bitten but you cannot effectively clean the wound, a consultation with your vet is worthwhile. The vet may prescribe antibiotics to prevent infection developing. A short course given early can save a lot of problems later.

Dog bites

A dog bite can cause severe bruising and deep tissue injury as well as producing irregular, torn wounds in the skin. What you can see on the surface might be only a small part of the actual damage. Veterinary attention and treatment for shock, infection, bruising and possibly internal damage is strongly recommended following a dog bite.

First aid

Large open wounds should be covered with a pad of clean, preferably sterile, absorbent material such as gauze. A handkerchief might do. Bandage it firmly in place, with a roll bandage or strips of cloth. In an emergency, a scarf, tie or handkerchief will suffice. Do not remove the lowermost pad or you might disturb partly formed blood clots.

In areas where rabies is present it must be determined whether the biting animal has been vaccinated. If a vicious attack by a wild animal has occurred, every effort should be made to destroy that animal and have it examined for rabies.

Beware: Do not touch an animal if you suspect it might have rabies, even when it is dead. Wear gloves, and wrap the body in a large plastic bag or a blanket before picking it up.

BROKEN BONES (FRACTURES)

There is a common misconception that a 'fracture' is somehow worse than a 'break' in the bone. This is not so. Both words mean the same thing.

Signs
- *Loss of function:* The cat will not use a broken leg or tail. It will dangle and is usually held at an abnormal angle.
- *Pain:* Cats usually tolerate a fracture remarkably well, although they will object strongly if the broken bone is moved or handled roughly. Otherwise cats usually cope with pain without much apparent fuss.

- *Swelling:* The affected limb usually becomes very swollen. The swelling can be difficult to see if the femur (upper hind limb) is broken. If one of the lower bones is broken, swelling is generally obvious by an hour after the accident.

First aid
It is rarely either necessary or possible to apply a splint. Your main objective is to transport the cat to your vet in the most comfortable, practicable manner. Your aim is to cause the minimum extra trauma.

Preferably, put the cat into a cat basket or a secure cardboard box where it cannot move around too much. If a suitable box is not available and if the cat is calm, you should carry the cat (refer to the diagrams). Allow the injured limb to hang free.

Foreleg fracture
Hold the cat by the scruff and support its weight by placing a hand under the rump, as shown in the diagram above.

Hindleg fracture
Hold the cat by the scruff and support the weight by placing a hand under the chest.

Fractured pelvis
As for hindleg.

Back (spinal) injury
If there is loss of function or sensation in both hind legs, or in all four legs *beware:* the cat might have suffered spinal damage. Handle the cat with extreme care to avoid further damage.

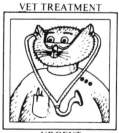

VET TREATMENT

URGENT

It is essential to transport the cat with the absolute minimum of movement of the suspected fracture site. Do *not* bend the cat's back at any stage. Put the cat on to a large, firm board, or place the cat carefully into a large box so that it can lie flat. A blanket can be used, but because it sags you should support the cat's weight by

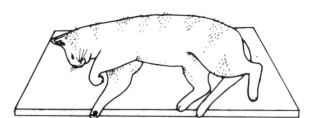

Transport a cat with suspected back injuries on a flat, firm board

placing one or both hands under the blanket and cat as it is being carried along. At all times keep the back as straight as possible.

CHOKING

Signs

Mouth agape, tongue protruding and saliva flowing. Cat makes convulsive coughing and choking noises and might paw at mouth. Legs splayed, head down and neck extended.

Vets are frequently telephoned by owners who believe that their cat is choking to death. In the vast majority of these cases, the cat is merely gagging on some irritating matter such as phlegm or a wad of hair. The noise produced as they make these expulsive efforts mimics the sounds humans make when they are indeed choking. In the cat, these retching and coughing sounds and efforts can be alarming. If the cat is not particularly distressed there is usually little to be concerned about. However, if the signs listed above *are* present, see your vet immediately.

First aid

Do not put your fingers into the cat's mouth or you will be bitten. Use one of the following techniques:

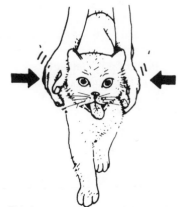

- If you can see the object and it is not irregularly shaped or sharp or pointed, then you might be able to grasp it with needle-nosed pliers or tweezers and pull it out.
- Place one hand flat over each side of the cat's chest and give a quick squeeze. The

This is one way to try to dislodge matter stuck in the throat

sudden thrust of air that results might dislodge and eject the foreign body from the cat's throat.

- Hold the cat by the scruff of the neck and by the hind legs. Turn the cat upside down and shake it vigorously for a few seconds.
- If the cat's gums are turning blue and its eyes are bulging, then this is an emergency. Place a chock in the mouth so that the cat cannot bite you. A piece of wood, a knife handle or a ruler will do. After chocking the mouth open so that it cannot close around your finger, try to hook the object out with a finger.

ARTIFICIAL RESPIRATION

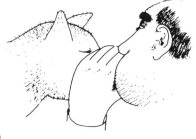

Artificial respiration might be needed after: drowning, smoke inhalation, choking, or electric shock.

Treatment

When breathing has stopped but the heart is still beating:

- Remove any foreign matter from the mouth. (Use tweezers or pliers, *not* your finger.)
- In the case of drowning, hold the cat upside down, shaking it gently.
- Lie cat on side.
- Stretch neck forward, with head up.
- Pull tongue out as far as you can. This opens up the throat.
- Press down over the chest with the flat of your hand

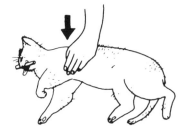

Artificial respiration: Place a chock in the mouth if necessary. Keep your fingers clear

using a short, sharp push that forcibly ejects the air. Repeat every 5 seconds until the cat begins to breathe spontaneously.

FITS AND CONVULSIONS

The spectacle of a cat having a fit can be alarming. Don't rush in with an ill-considered attempt to help. In most cases there is little you can do until the convulsive episode is over. Most fits last only a minute or so and end spontaneously.

If the fit is continuous or recurring, you need a vet's help urgently. Move the cat only if absolutely necessary, and then do so with caution, preferably with the cat enveloped in a large, thick blanket.

Signs
Some of the following might occur:
- Muscle twitching and spasm.
- Cat might collapse, usually on to one side.
- Neck arches back.
- Legs held rigid, or paddling with forepaws.
- Might pass urine or faeces.

Most fits only last from 2–5 minutes. Some last only a few seconds, and owners frequently fail to realise that the episode was a fit. In some cases the fit might last half an hour or longer, or there may be recurring fits with only short intervals between.

After the fit there is a variable period in which the cat will seem a bit dazed. It might react in a quite abnormal, even bizarre fashion. Some become frightened and run to hide. These cats should be approached only with caution as they are unpredictable until they settle down and might uncharacteristically bite or scratch. Others will seek out their owner for sympathy or comfort.

Treatment
If possible, leave the cat alone until the fit has passed. It is dangerous to handle a convulsing cat. The cat will not recognise you, and you could be bitten or scratched. The cat could give the impression of being in pain. In fact it is not in pain, and we believe it will remember nothing of the actual fit later.

If the cat is in a dangerous position, such as in the middle of a road or on the balcony of a high-rise building, it might be essential to move it. First, throw a blanket, coat or large towel over the cat. Then, after wrapping it up, move the whole bundle to safety.

Keep the convulsing, or recently recovered, cat quiet and undisturbed, preferably in a dark room. Remove or extinguish any potentially dangerous objects such as electric heaters or fans. Draw the curtains. Switch off any source of noise such as the TV.

Possible causes of fits
- Poisons (see the section on poisons later in this chapter).
- Infections (e.g. toxoplasmosis).
- Eclampsia (milk fever).

- Chronic kidney and liver diseases.
- Epilepsy.
- Brain tumour.
- Post-accident blood clot or scarring.
- Worms (especially in kittens).

HAIRBALLS

Because cats are fastidious about their coats they normally groom themselves daily. Inevitably some dead hairs are raked out by the cat's barbed tongue and subsequently swallowed. The cat's digestive system is perfectly capable of handling even quite large amounts of hair without the cat suffering any discomfort. At certain times, for example in spring or when the cat is sick, quite large amounts of hair are consumed, and a 'hairball' might be formed in the cat's throat or stomach.

When a mass of hair balls up in the stomach it could prevent the normal passage of food. Eventually the hairball will either pass through into the small intestine or the cat will vomit it up as a cigar-shaped mass. This vomiting appears disagreeable, but it does not cause the cat any harm. It is natural and normal, and not a cause for alarm.

A cat with a hairball might feel hungry but eats only a little at a time, presumably because the hairball gives it a bloated feeling.

Hairballs are just a part of life for many cats. Having to watch a cat vomit a hairball can be disturbing for many owners. Don't get too upset. Once the cat has expelled the offending mass of hair it will feel much better. If, however, the cat continually gags and retches but fails to produce the offending irritant, then you should contact your vet.

First aid

You can ease the passage of a hairball by giving a non-toxic lubricant, such as mineral oil, liquid paraffin or white petroleum jelly. We prefer liquid paraffin, ½–1 teaspoon daily until the hairball is cleared.

Many commercial hairball 'cures' are available. These are generally prepared so as to be quite attractive to cats and are therefore often easier to administer than liquid paraffin.

Prevention

Regular brushing or combing will reduce the formation of hair-balls and perhaps even prevent them altogether. Extra grooming is especially valuable in spring when most cats moult.

HEATSTROKE

Heatstroke is usually associated with confinement in a hot, poorly ventilated area such as a parked car, in a cat box exposed to direct sunlight or in a tin shed. Deprivation of water exacerbates the situation. Cats with flat faces, such as Persians, are more susceptible to heatstroke, as are very old or very young cats.

Signs

Open mouth, rapid breathing, salivation. Gums very red at first but later becoming bluish. Cat becomes very distressed. Eventually will collapse into a coma.

Death could follow.

Treatment

You must cool the cat and provide good ventilation.
- Remove it from the hot area (for example, parked car with windows shut).
- Allow plenty of fresh air.
- Cool the cat, using a water spray or cloths soaked in cool water *or* immerse the cat up to its neck in a cool water bath.
- After recovery, allow free access to clean drinking water.

The cat's condition should improve within about 10 minutes, although you might have to continue cooling for up to half an hour. *Beware:* Do not overdo the cooling as the cat could become chilled. The water should be cool but not icy.

Veterinary advice should be sought after the cat's temperature has been brought down. There is some danger of cerebral oedema (swelling of the brain) developing.

Prevention

Prevention is mainly common sense and forethought.

- Never leave your cat confined in a parked car or similar confined space when the weather is hot (higher than 25°C).
- On hot days, allow the cat plenty of air circulation and free access to water and shade.

COLD INJURY

Cold injury (hypothermia) is caused by exposure to cold water or freezing temperatures, especially if the cat is wet or in a debilitated state. Sometimes cats are accidentally locked in a fridge. Newborn kittens are highly susceptible to cold stress. If the cat's body temperature falls below 32°C normal body functions will be severely depressed.

Signs
At first shivering. As the body temperature drops, the cat becomes lethargic and eventually unconscious. The body is very cold to the touch, especially at the extremities, such as ear tips. Breathing is slow and shallow.

Treatment
If the cat is wet, first dry it thoroughly. Avoid all draughts. Then apply heat. *Do not* try to heat the cat too quickly as the sudden application of heat can cause shock and collapse, and perhaps extensive tissue damage. Put the cat into a warm room, but not too close to the heater or fire.

If the cat has collapsed, or in the case of a chilled newborn kitten, immersion in a warm water bath is an excellent way of heating the cat. After the cat has warmed, remove it from the bath and dry it thoroughly. Then keep it in a warm, draught-free area for several hours.

Warm milk and food may be offered. If the cat is not interested, do not attempt to force feed it.

FROSTBITE

Ear tips and tails are particularly prone to frostbite.

Signs
Affected area feels very cold and lacks any sensation. It might be very pale or a bluish colour.

Treatment
Apply warm cotton wool pads. First soak the pads in warm water, then squeeze out excess fluid. Do not rub the injured area or you might damage the skin. Keep changing the pads or rewarming them. Seek veterinary advice. If the damage is too severe the affected area might require amputation.

OBJECTS CAUGHT IN THE MOUTH

Do not put your fingers into the cat's mouth. Even very placid cats can unintentionally bite. The cat has a very sensitive throat, and you might inadvertently trigger off a reflex reaction, causing the cat to bite down on your finger.

Fish hook in lip
Do not try to pull the hook out. If possible, have your vet remove the hook. Otherwise, cut the hook in half with wire cutters or pliers so that the barb falls off. Then the hook can quickly be slid out of the cat's lip.

Thread
Beware: There could be a needle on the other end. Cats enjoy playing with thread, but the thread can easily become hooked around the barbs on the cat's tongue. It is then inexorably worked back into the throat and swallowed. If you suspect a needle could be on the other end, you should *not* attempt to pull the thread out. Seek veterinary advice immediately.

Other foreign objects (e.g. bones, hair or grass seeds)

Use a pair of tweezers or needle-nose pliers if you are trying to remove foreign matter from your cat's mouth. Thread, grass or other debris tangled around the teeth can best be removed by lifting the lip back. Work from the outside of the teeth. This is easier than trying to open the jaws and probe around inside.

If you need to open the mouth and probe inside, for example to remove a bone lodged across the roof of the mouth, you should prepare well first. Get someone to help in restraining the cat. Preferably wrap the cat in a towel first. Put the cat on a table where the light is good. A pencil torch is helpful and can be held in your mouth, leaving both hands free. Do not put your fingers into the cat's mouth. Use tweezers, pliers or similar.

MOTOR CAR ACCIDENTS

After a motor car accident (or similar trauma) the cat will be in a state of shock. It will be frightened and perhaps in pain. Approach carefully and slowly. The cat is liable to be very defensive and could be aggressive even to people it knows well. Talk to the cat quietly. Don't make sudden movements or grab for the cat. Even if the cat is lying dazed, be careful—it might partially recover and scratch or bite in fear.

Ideally, you should wear long leather gloves such as motorcycle gauntlets. These will only rarely be available, so use the best substitute you can. A coat, large towel, or rug may be thrown over the cat and it can then be hooked up. If the cat is fairly calm, expose its head (but *only* its head).

Be prepared—the cat will probably wriggle and struggle. Don't let go unless you absolutely must. Any future attempts to catch the cat will be far more difficult than the first. If you pick up the cat, hold it by the scruff and place it as soon as practicable into a cat box or other suitable container. If the cat escapes, do not chase it helter-skelter. Watch where it goes, then approach slowly. A calm approach has a much better chance of success.

Depending on the nature of the cat's injury, proceed as outlined for shock and/or bleeding, fractures, cuts and bruises.

STINGS AND INSECT BITES

Bee, wasp, hornet or spider stings can cause considerable distress. Kittens indulging in play-hunting are especially liable.

Signs

Intense pain at the site of the sting. Site becomes swollen, red and hot to the touch. With spider bites or multiple wasp or bee stings, there might also be:

- Vomiting.
- Muscle twitching.
- Shivering.

If the bite is around the mouth there could be localised swelling in the throat or tongue. This is an emergency. Urgent veterinary attention is required. There are no effective first aid measures if the cat's throat is obstructed by swelling.

Otherwise:

- If the sting is visible, pull it out with tweezers.
- If the cat will cooperate, apply cotton wool soaked in vinegar to the bitten area. An antihistamine cream, if available, may help.

SNAKE BITES

Cats are not often bitten by snakes.

If you suspect a snake bite you should consider the following: Is the snake poisonous? Many snakes are not. In the USA and Europe, most snakes are non-venomous. In Australia, almost *all* are venomous. In New Zealand there are no snakes. The pattern of the bite wound can be helpful in deciding whether the snake was venomous.

Non-venomous bite

- U-shaped bite marks. These might be difficult to see because of the cat's fur.
- There is some pain but very little swelling.

Treatment

As for any bite wound. Assume that the wound is contaminated with bacteria. Clip away the fur. Flush with 2% hydrogen peroxide or mild soap and water. Many cats will resent your handling of the wound but will clean it themselves. In these cases it might not be necessary to interfere unless the wound subsequently shows signs of swelling, redness and pain. This could indicate that infection is developing.

Venomous bite

True signs of snake bite vary with the type of venom injected. Snake venom usually have a mix of various toxins. The ratio of toxins varies with the genus of snake.

Signs

Signs usually start within 20 minutes but can take up to an hour. These signs vary with the venom type and dose of venom injected.

- Acute, painful swelling at wound site. (This does not always occur. There might be only a minimal local reaction.)
- Paralysis, including breathing difficulty or 'shortness of breath'.
- Presence of typical fang marks. Difficult to see due to cat's fur.
- Vomiting, distress.
- Blood in the urine.

Treatment

Many strikes are around the head. In entire toms or cats with thick coats there is a good chance that the snake's fangs will not penetrate the skin because of its thickness and the fur.

When the skin *is* broken and venom is injected you have two aims: to slow the spread of venom and to get to the vet as soon as possible.

- Flush the wound with water to remove venom.
- Keep the cat as still as practicable.
- If a limb or tail was bitten, apply a Robert Jones dressing.
- If the bite is on the head or neck, apply ice to the wound if the cat will tolerate it.
- Put the cat into a small container or box to restrict its activity. Movement increases the rate of spread of the venom.

The Robert Jones dressing: first apply a large amount of cotton wool. Layer it on in sheets. An elastic adhesive bandage is then firmly applied over the cotton wool. Start at the bottom of the foot and work up. The Robert Jones dressing can also be used as a temporary splint in fracture cases — even in large cats, dogs or horses

Tourniquets

Never apply a tight tourniquet on a cat. If you cannot apply a Robert Jones dressing, then apply pressure a few centimetres above the wound (between the wound and the heart) using a broad bandage (a tie or belt will do). Apply this *firmly,* not tightly.

Ice packs

Crush some ice, put it into a plastic bag or a sock, then hold it over the bite wound. This will slow the absorption of venom from the strike site. A packet of frozen peas or beans from the freezer also makes a convenient ice pack.

VET TREATMENT

URGENT

Veterinary treatment

Anti-venoms will neutralise the toxins. The *correct* anti-venom is important. If you have killed the snake, take it to the vet with you. Otherwise try to remember any distinguishing features, especially its size, the colour of both back and belly, and any striping or pattern. Any other notable feature such as a flat head, or a broad tail, could be useful.

Treatment by your vet might include antivenom, treatment for shock, pain, internal bleeding and/or kidney damage.

Incising the wound

Incising the wound is *not* recommended.

TICK PARALYSIS

See chapter 18 on nerves for discussion of tick paralysis.

SHOCK

A state of shock is serious. *Shock* does not mean just a 'fright'. Shock is a series of physiological changes that occur in the body after injury. *Shock can kill.* Many cats injured in road accidents or severely burned, etc., die from shock. The causes of shock include:

- Severe diarrhoea and vomiting.
- Blood loss.
- Fluid loss, for example from burns.
- Severe bruising.
- Blood poisoning, for example from extensive bite infection.
- Snake bite.

- Car accidents.

Signs
- Rapid, shallow breathing or panting (cats rarely pant—if they do so they are generally in considerable distress).
- Pale, cold or bluish-coloured gums. (Lift the side of a lip back to examine them.)
- Paws and ears feel cold.
- Pulse or heartbeat is weak and rapid.
- Cat might be immobile and unwilling to stand, flopping down again if picked up. Might be flaccid and unresponsive.
- Fails to respond normally to being called, stroked or picked up.
- Pupils dilated (wide open). Might have a 'glazed' look about the eyes.

Treatment
Time is important. Start treatment as soon as possible. Don't let shock continue to develop.
- Keep the cat warm, dry and draught free. If necessary, wrap the cat in a blanket and put into a warm room or apply heat indirectly, for example, using a water bottle. Beware of overheating the cat. Do not place it too close to a fire or place the hot water bottle directly on to the coat. Overheating can make shock worse.
- Reassure the cat—calm, quiet talking and slow, gentle stroking can be extremely effective.
- Don't disturb the cat too much if it resents attention.
- If the cat wants to drink, give warm milk or glucose and water. *Do not* try to force liquids.

Where shock is severe, veterinary attention is essential, or the cat will die. If you have to transport the cat, keep it warm and move it gently. It is better to drive slowly than to race anxiously and further alarm the cat.

VOMITING

A cat vomits to clear its stomach of any irritating or noxious substances, for example, hairballs, spoiled food or toxic chemicals. In many instances, once the offending matter has been eliminated, the problem is over, and there is no need for treatment other than to 'rest' the stomach. Sometimes vomiting can be a sign of a serious disorder. Vomiting can occur as one clinical sign in the following conditions. This list is not exhaustive:
- Obstructions of the bowel.
- Liver, pancreas or kidney disease.

- Swelling within any abdominal organ, for example a tumour of the spleen or a blocked bladder.
- Food poisoning.
- Viral infection, for example feline infectious enteritis.

Treatment

If your cat has vomited but otherwise is alert and not in pain, proceed as follows:

- Remove all food and water.
- After 8–12 hours offer water. If it stays down a few hours later, offer a small amount of food. A spoonful is enough. Give a food that you know the cat likes, but avoid fatty, oily or rich foods. Cooked, minced chicken or fish is suitable.
- Offer water, but do not allow the cat to drink more than about a tablespoonful at a time.
- For the next 24 hours offer only small meals.
- Return the cat to the normal diet gradually.
- Don't rush. Take 2–5 days. This allows the stomach to settle down.

Consult your vet if

- The vomit contains blood.
- Vomiting is frequent or persistent.
- Vomiting is accompanied by profuse diarrhoea.
- The cat is lethargic, distressed or in pain.

DIARRHOEA

Many cats are private or secretive about their bowel motions. You might not actually be able to see a motion. Suspect diarrhoea if your cat is making frequent trips to the toilet area, or if the fur around the anus and hocks is matted or stained, or if the anus is raw and inflamed. (Frequent trips to the toilet area can also indicate cystitis.)

Most cats will have an occasional bout of diarrhoea. In many cases no treatment is necessary, but if the diarrhoea is severe or persistent then read the section on diarrhoea in chapter 14 on the gut and consult your vet if necessary.

Treatment
- Withhold food for 24 hours.
- Give water only. No milk.
- After 24 hours, offer small amounts of a readily digestible food such as cooked, minced chicken. Add boiled rice if the cat will accept it.
- Only gradually return to the normal diet.

Various anti-diarrhoea preparations are commercially available. They could help to speed a cure. For example, use Kaomagma (aluminium hydroxide gel) or Kaopectate. Dose: ½–1 teaspoon twice daily.

Consult your vet if
- The cat is very lethargic.
- Vomiting accompanies the diarrhoea.
- There is blood in the motion.
- Diarrhoea persists or recurs after treatment is withdrawn.

FALL FROM A HEIGHT

Over-ambitious or frightened cats might jump from a height that is beyond their capabilities. Sometimes a cat might jump at a bird that lands on a window sill, or perhaps a branch might give way as it climbs a tree. Usually a cat will survive it it falls from below a height of three storeys. Above that the outcome depends on the nature of the ground it falls on.

Cats almost always land on all four feet. In some cases the cat's chin will smack on to the ground, so a fracture of the lower jaw is a common result of a fall from a height. The cat might also lose teeth and split the roof of its mouth. One or more legs could be fractured. Other injuries could possibly include shock and perhaps rupture of internal organs such as the liver, kidney and spleen.

POISONING

Cats are very careful about what they eat. As a result malicious poisonings are rare. But there are other ways in which a cat might be exposed to toxic doses of a variety of dangerous compounds. Sometimes an owner might inadvertently give drugs that the cat's system cannot cope with. Many substances are relatively non-toxic to humans but dangerous to cats. Cats cannot readily detoxify or degrade these substances into harmless by-products. Common examples are aspirin, paracetamol, benzoic acid (a preservative) and phenolic compounds.

Another relatively common way in which cats are exposed to poisons is when their coat is contaminated by them. The cat's meticulous grooming instincts drive it to clear away any foreign matter. Unfortunately, potentially toxic substances, such as insecticides, disinfectants, cleansers, lead paints or adhesives, could be present. The correct first aid procedures, applied as soon after exposure as possible, can be critical to the outcome. There are thousands of toxic materials. Seek immediate telephone advice before going to your vet. Some of the most common poisons and the appropriate type of immediate first aid are discussed below.

Cats sometimes ingest poisonous substances when they groom themselves

Acetaminophen/ paracetamol

Acetaminophen and paracetamol are two names for the same drug, which reduces pain and relieves fever. The name varies from country to country.

This drug is usually given to the cat by owners who are unaware that it can be deadly. Some cats die within 24 hours because the drug attacks the red cells. Some others survive that phase but become ill 3–4 days later as the drug destroys the liver. Signs include gums turning from pink to a brownish colour, blood in urine, abdominal pain, difficulty in breathing, and death. You need veterinary help as soon as possible.

Antifreeze

Some cats will lick at antifreeze (ethylene glycol) because it is sweet-tasting. It causes physical depression, loss of consciousness, and coma. Induce vomiting if possible, and go straight to your vet.

Aspirin

Cats can tolerate low doses of aspirin (10 mg per kg, which is about ⅙ of a standard tablet) but have difficulty excreting it, so repeated dosage can have a cumulative effect. Signs of poisoning include lack of coordination, loss of balance, excessive sensitivity to sound and touch, and vomiting (sometimes bloody). Induce vomiting if aspirin was recently given (i.e. within the hour); otherwise give milk and/or activated charcoal.

Carbon monoxide

Carbon monoxide poisoning is seen mainly if a cat becomes trapped in a garage or similar situation. Poisoning occurs rapidly. Gums turn a distinct cherry red, and there is difficulty breathing. Get the cat out and into fresh air. Oxygen is life-saving, but sometimes there is not enough time.

Organophosphates

Organophosphates are included in many flea treatments, including some collars and rinses as well as insect sprays and pellets. Poisoning by organophosphate is quite common. Signs of intoxication are profuse salivation, vomiting, diarrhoea, muscle twitching and spasms, lack of coordination and maybe seizures.

Treatment is to rinse any remaining material off the cat's coat immediately and proceed to the vet. There is an antidote if treatment is commenced early.

Rat baits/poisons

Most rat baits or poisons cause bleeding, so the signs include pale gums, difficult or rapid breathing and lethargy. This type of poisoning can be produced by eating poisoned rodents. There is a very effective antidote to the Warfarin-type baits if started early. Some other types, notably those containing cholecalciferol, induce massive organ damage and kidney failure, and the outlook is very poor.

For most poisons the most important thing to be able to tell your vet is the *active ingredient*—not just the brand name—if you are to get the most appropriate advice and treatment.

Strychnine

Strychnine is the most common malicious poison. Initially the cat is apprehensive and irritable, progressing to violent convulsions.

The cat is very sensitive to touch and to noise. Transport it to the vet in a padded box, avoiding loud noise or sudden movement.

Inducing vomiting

Do not induce vomiting until you have checked with your veterinarian, and only induce vomiting if the cat is fully conscious.

There are various ways of stimulating the cat to vomit. *Do not* try to stick a finger down the cat's throat. You will inevitably be bitten, no matter how placid the cat, as its jaw will clamp shut in a reflex action.

Give *one* of the following:
* Syrup of Ipecac—dose 2 ml per kg body weight (usual dose for an adult cat: 8 ml). This syrup is available from pharmacists.
* Salt and water: make up a solution by dissolving 2 heaped teaspoons common table salt in ½ cup water. Try to give the cat 10 ml or more.
* ½ teaspoon salt placed on the back of the tongue.
* 1 teaspoon raw mustard.
* Hydrogen peroxide (3% solution). Dose: 5 ml.

3 NATURAL MEDICINE

Many medicines available for use in humans, dogs and other species are not suitable for cats. There is, however, a gradual increase in the use of natural therapies for cats as they appear to be safe and can sometimes be remarkably effective.

Natural medicine involves the use of non-invasive, natural methods to stimulate the cat's own healing abilities, allowing its return to an optimum or 'balanced' state from one of imbalance or disease. Cats are unaware of the alleged effects of these treatments, so it is extremely interesting to note the apparent response of some patients to these treatment methods.

Veterinarians are trained to follow a scientific approach with proven basis and rational explanations for their effects. Many therefore have difficulty in accepting natural therapy. However, the number of practitioners who either use these methods themselves or are happy to refer clients to natural therapists has increased recently.

ACUPUNCTURE

Acupuncture is the clearest example of an alternative medicine that has broken through enormous barriers of scepticism and disbelief to become an integral part of mainstream veterinary practice. Acupuncture was virtually unknown until the 1960s as a treatment for animals, and its mode of action is still not certain. However, the results of acupuncture treatment for animals are now incontestable, and it is therefore now available in most parts of the western world.

Acupuncture is also one of the safest forms of therapy if practised by a competent acupuncturist. Courses in veterinary acupuncture are heavily subscribed to. Successful participants are awarded a certificate by the International Veterinary Acupuncture Association (IVAS). As a result acupuncture is available to most cat owners living in major population centres.

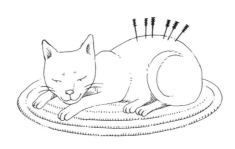

The basic theory behind acupuncture is that there is a life force within the body called ch'i, which is depleted by daily living but replenished by food and water. Energy moves within the body in channels, called meridians, which run in pairs throughout the body. Any disruption to this flow can cause either a depletion of or build up of ch'i. Acupuncture is believed to help rebalance ch'i through the stimulation of reflex points, sited along the meridians. Body maps are available for many species with these reflex points marked on them.

Cats have potentially excellent powers of healing. Acupuncture is believed to stimulate these powers strongly or, as the acupuncturists prefer to put it, to channel them.

Many owners and veterinarians have been reluctant to try acupuncture because they fear that the cat will react defensively to needle insertion. However, in experienced hands, most cats will tolerate this insertion without fuss and will sit quietly for the 10–15 minutes of treatment. Animals that have had acupuncture are often very relaxed and calm about subsequent treatments, so it seems to be a pleasant experience for them.

When the needles have been inserted most patients appear calm, even sedated. The needles, which are very fine, are then stimulated in a variety of ways—sometimes by heating, using tiny electric currents, burning a variety of herbs or just by manual spinning. Sometimes substances such as vitamins, pure water or drugs are injected. In difficult cases, a laser apparatus can be used to stimulate acupuncture points.

Acupuncture has been tried as therapy for most conditions, but some respond better than others. In general a longstanding, or chronic, condition is likely to need several treatments before improvement becomes apparent, while recently acquired diseases are usually more dramatic both in onset and in response to treatment.

Diseases and conditions that might respond to acupuncture therapy include:

- Idiopathic bladder irritation, i.e. a condition whose cause cannot be determined and therefore conventional methods of treatment are often unsuccessful.
- Dermatitis, particularly allergic skin conditions, but the underlying cause must also be treated.
- Arthritis.
- Upper respiratory tract infections (e.g. cat flu).
- Chronic sinusitis.
- Gingivitis, especially in cases where the teeth are healthy but the gums are red and inflamed.
- Eye conditions, such as epiphora, conjunctivitis, dry eye and indolent ulcers.

- Neurological disorders, such as encephalopathy or vestibular disease.
- Chronic diarrhoea.
- Constipation due to megacolon.
- Emergency conditions (e.g. shock syndrome).
- Geriatrics: acupuncture can improve the quality of life in the geriatric patient.

In addition some viral diseases might benefit from the use of acupuncture, because acupuncture increases the immune response, reduces fever, stimulates appetite and reduces recovery time. Cats with feline leukaemia, feline immunodeficiency virus and feline infectious peritonitis might have longer survival time and better quality of life with acupuncture therapy.

Acupuncture can be used in conjunction with antibiotics to aid in the treatment of bacterial infections.

AROMATHERAPY

The practice of using essential oils, such as frankincense, lavender and clove, pre-dates the ancient Egyptian era during which it became prominent. Most people recognise how evocative a smell can be, and to animals smells or aromas are likely to be far more significant as their sense of smell is far better developed than it is in humans.

It is likely that aromatherapy works by stimulating the hypothalamus, a small organ within the brain, which is sometimes termed the 'brain's brain', and which in turn stimulates and promotes the body's immune system.

Essential oils are extracted from various parts of plants. The oils are antibacterial, antifungal, antiviral and antiseptic, and 70% stronger in this form than in the original plants. While they can have beneficial effects on physical and mental health of cats, they must never be given internally, or chemical poisoning might occur. They must be diluted: 1 drop oil to 10 ml water or massage oil. They can then either be combed or massaged through the coat or used on bedding, as a room spray or in a vaporiser.

Lavender and camomile are great oils for general stress, and help relieve anxiety and tension. Eucalyptus is soothing for anger, and is a good decongestant; peppermint is stimulating to the mind but

Table 2: Properties of essential oils

Essential oil	Healing properties/uses
Basil	Soothing, clears the brain
Camomile	Soothing
Clove	Antiseptic, analgesic, respiratory complaints
Eucalyptus	Head clearing, antiseptic, anti-inflammatory, analgesic
Frankincense	Nerve tonic
Jasmine	Relaxing
Lavender	Head clearing, sedative, calming, antiseptic
Lemon	Antiseptic, refreshing
Myrrh	Anti-inflammatory, antiseptic
Peppermint	Anti-inflammatory
Rosemary	Stimulating
Sage	Relaxing
Tea-tree	Antiseptic, flea and mosquito control, respiratory infection
Thyme	Antiseptic

calming to the stomach, and tea-tree is one of the most potent antiseptics. Geranium might help skin disorders, especially if hormonally related in females.

Further advice on these remedies is available from practising holistic veterinarians, stockists or texts.

HERBS

Plants have been used for medicinal purposes for thousands of years, and herbalists claim to be practitioners of true traditional medicine. Almost all the ancient peoples had their equivalent of a herbal pharmacist, usually surrounded by an aura of magic, whose skills were handed down orally and whose secrets were jealously guarded.

Herbs can be used to treat many health problems in cats. They appear to work by boosting the immune system and general vitality of the cat. Their use should be monitored carefully as individuals react differently. Identification of the correct herbs and their subsequent preparation requires expert knowledge and experience, so seek advice before becoming too enthusiastic about home experimentation. Some plants are highly toxic and dangerous even in tiny amounts.

Herbal remedies

When deciding whether a herbal ointment or solution is safe to use on your cat, remember that cats can lick off any ointment, oil, or solution that is put on their skin. If the herb is safe to be taken internally by humans, it is generally safe to use as an external ointment or solution on a cat. If it is for *external use only* in humans, do not put it on a cat's skin. Following is a list of some common disease conditions and herbal remedies that may be used in their treatment.

Bladder (cystitis)
Bladder irritation or infection may be treated with cornsilk, couchgrass, and uva ursi tinctures. When treating a male, cleavers (also called goosegrass) may be useful.

Bronchitis
Two good lung-strengthening and cleansing herbs are elecampagne and coltsfoot. If bacterial infection is suspected, use garlic and echinacea as well. For viral coughs use red clover, garlic, and echinacea initially, and elecampagne or coltsfoot later if the cat needs an extra boost to aid recovery.

Diabetes
See pancreatitis (below).

Diarrhoea
Slippery elm bark powder may be used in any case of diarrhoea to help soothe the gut.

Ears
For chronically inflamed and 'dirty' ears use warm olive oil to clean and soothe the ear.

Eczema
For itchy, red, weeping skin, pawpaw ointment or fresh pawpaw skin should give quick symptomatic relief if applied twice a day to the affected area. You will then need to deal with the cause of the eczema.

Eyes
Red, inflamed eyes might respond well to bathing with camomile tea. If infection is also present, bathe the eyes with calendula tincture diluted 5 drops to ½ cup water. Golden seal and/or cheledonium tincture may be mixed with calendula in equal parts and diluted 5 drops of the mixture to ½ cup water.

Fractures

There is no herbal replacement for proper stabilisation of a fractured bone. However, once the fracture has been stabilised with a splint or surgical intervention, comfrey and equisetum, commonly known as horsetail, should be given to speed healing.

Grass seeds

Castor oil is very useful to 'float out' a grass seed whether it be in the eye, ear or foot. Put 1–2 drops directly into the eye, a dropper full into the ear, or a cotton wool ball soaked in castor oil under a bandage on the foot.

If the grass seed is still in the eye or ear by the next morning, seek veterinary attention immediately. If in the foot, it is safe to continue treating with castor oil for another 24–48 hours.

Heart

For cats with early congestive heart failure a safe, gentle heart remedy is hawthorn tincture.

Infections

When there is bacterial or viral infection anywhere in the body use garlic, vitamin C, and echinacea tincture or tablets to help the body 'fight' the invaders.

Kidneys

Kidney inflammation and/or infection may be treated with golden rod tincture for 3–4 days, as well as with buchu and shepherd's purse for a longer time. Garlic and echinacea may be added when infection is present. If you suspect kidney problems in your cat seek veterinary attention *before* attempting any home remedy.

Liver

Whether the liver is diseased or just overworked from too many toxins in the body, dandelion will help. Dandelion may be given as tincture, tablets, tea or fresh green leaves, depending on the severity of the liver problem.

Muscles

Muscle spasms associated with trauma, surgery, and spinal disc disease will often relax when treated with valerian tincture or tablets.

Nervous cats

A combination of skullcap and valerian, in either tincture or tablet form, helps overly excited or nervous cats to calm down.

Pancreatitis

Fennel is the primary herb for pancreatic problems. If diabetes is present, a combination of fennel and dandelion is safe to use even when the cat is on insulin.

Wounds

For dirty or puncture wounds first use castor oil to float out all the dirt and then apply calendula ointment and bandage if possible. A second application of castor oil might be needed the next day, and the calendula ointment should be used until the wound is healed. For clean, open, and/or bleeding wounds, use calendula ointment and a handful of crushed yarrow leaves to stop bleeding and promote healing. When giving tinctures orally to cats 1 drop daily is all that is needed in most cases. Tablets ⅛–¼ of the dosage recommended for adult humans may be given, depending on the size of the cat. Avoid giving herbs continuously. Even food herbs such as garlic should be discontinued periodically for periods of 2–5 days every month.

FLOWER ESSENCES

Flower essences should not be confused with aromatherapy and herbal medicine, both of which have been discussed. Flower essences can be useful in treating emotional stress and behavioural changes in cats. These essences were originally harvested by collecting the dew of flowers. The flowers are picked just as they bloom and after preparation are preserved in brandy. They appear to target personality characteristics and states of mind. They are non-toxic, safe and gentle, and so can easily be administered at home. You can also experiment with them as there are no ill effects if you use the wrong one.

The best known are the essences of British flowers, developed by the British physician, Dr Edward Bach, in the 1930s. Called the Bach flower essences, they are a set of thirty-eight remedies designed to be taken in liquid form a few drops at a time.

Most countries now make essences out of their own native flowers. For example there are now more than sixty Australian bush flower essences. They appear to be even more effective than Bach flowers, possibly because of the purity of development allowed by centuries of isolation in Australia. There are also Californian, Alaskan, Himalayan, and New Zealand flower essences and more.

Flower essences are not believed to work by causing any chemical reaction within the body. Practitioners believe that, like homoeopathy and acupuncture, they are a 'vibrational energy healing' form, causing or allowing changes in the body's energy patterns. This is still a strange concept for many of us, but physicists are now recognising and even photographing these energy fields or recording them in other ways.

Suitable remedies

Cats are very sensitive individuals, and experience a range of mental states. Shy, timid cats might respond to centaury, mimulus, dog rose or walnut. Honeysuckle is especially good in helping cats through the trauma of moving house. Aspen, rock rose, grey spider flower and mimulus are all remedies for fear, helping to settle a frightened cat. Jealousy is sometimes a problem in multi-cat households, and holly is very helpful for this. Vine and isopogen are used for dominating and demanding cats, while willow helps those that are resentful. Indiscriminate aggression in some cats may be reduced with mountain devil. Aggression directed mainly at one individual is more likely to respond to slender rice flower. Crab apple is a great 'cleanser' and is particularly good for skin problems, especially if the cat is over-grooming.

Rescue Remedy is a composite remedy of five Bach flower essences: star of Bethlehem, impatiens, clematis, cherry plum and rock rose. Together they act to help counter the effect of shock and trauma, terror and hysteria. While it does not substitute for veterinary care in an emergency, it is quite helpful, and in no way detrimental, to give a cat a few doses on the way to the vet clinic. Rescue Remedy can also help in milder cases of stress and trauma, e.g. minor injuries, fights, lengthy stays in catteries or in hospital after surgery.

Dosage

Flower essences can be purchased individually, as a stock bottle, from health food stores (dose for an adult cat: 1–2 drops Bach flower and 4 drops Australian bush flower). Alternatively, a dosage bottle personally tailored to your cat's individual character, after consultation, can be purchased from flower essence veterinarians. Dosage is then changed by dilution. Drops are placed directly on the gums or tongue, or in drinking water if necessary.

NATUROPATHY

Naturopathy is the treatment of disease or disorder without drugs, usually involving diet, exercise and massage. It is also known as nature cure. Naturopaths believe that the key elements to restoring body equilibrium and achieving good health include:
• Good nutrition.

- Uninterrupted rest (a moot point with cats, which appear not to need the relatively long periods of deep sleep that some species, including humans, do).
- Exercise.
- Clean air and environment.
- Emotional calm.

HOMOEOPATHY

Homoeopathy is a complex discipline of about two hundred years standing, although its principles have been known for a thousand more. Like many other natural therapies, it often appears to work, but the scientists among us cannot explain why.

Homoeopathy is based on the principle that 'like is cured by like', *but only in tiny doses.* For example, for bee stings, use bee stings. Homoeopaths would look at a condition in which there is heat, redness, swelling and pain, and use something from nature that produces the same signs (in this case bee venom).

The mechanism of action is uncertain, but it is postulated that instead of dampening down the body's reaction, the minute amount of bee venom alerts the body's defence mechanisms, allowing it to cope more adequately. The bee venom in this case would be diluted to one ten-thousandth of its original strength, which is nowhere near enough to cause any clinical signs, but is apparently enough to allow a counterattack against potential harmful effects of similarly acting materials. Homoeopathic remedies are diluted so much that virtually none of the original material would seem to be present. It is postulated that some form of imprint or energy vibration remains.

MASSAGE AND GROOMING

Massage and grooming are other types of manipulative therapies. Touch is a potent reward to a cat, but touch is not just important, it is vital to the cat's well-being.

Touch, through grooming, stroking and patting, or simply resting your hand on your cat, is a great way to bond, and it has been proven to lower the blood pressures of both parties.

4 THE SENSES

How well does a cat see, hear or smell? The cat lives in a world of sensations very different from the ones we perceive. In trying to understand the cat's behaviour we try to find explanations in terms of our own senses, but we will never be able really to comprehend the feline mind.

HEARING

The cat has developed a hunter's sense of hearing. Prowling cats hear sounds that are inaudible to the human ear. Their hearing ranges far into ultrasound, well beyond our capability. Cats do more than just detect sound—they can also locate its source. The cat has twelve muscles in each ear that can accurately direct the ear towards a sound source, allowing the cat to zero in on a potential meal or source of danger. A cat can discriminate between two sound sources only 5 degrees apart—that is, the width of only four fingers at a range of more than a metre.

Cats are born deaf, but their hearing develops quickly. Try rustling a piece of crumpled cellophane near a 10 week-old

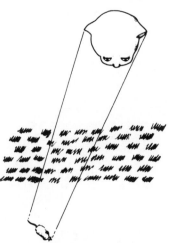

The cat can accurately detect the direction from which a sound has come. The cat knows where the mouse is even though a hedge screens it from view.

kitten. The high-frequency noises mimic the sounds made by small prey and usually trigger play-stalking and catching actions.

The cat's sense of hearing remains on guard even when the cat is asleep, or 'cat napping'. The slightest unusual sound arouses the cat back to full alert. Cats are also sensitive to vibrations felt through the pads of their feet, and are said to 'hear' with their feet.

As acute as their sense of hearing is, cats cannot hunt effectively in total darkness. Sight and touch are also essential for successful hunting.

With advancing age, the cat's hearing acuity diminishes. This is because the sensitive structures of the inner ear become less mobile and respond less efficiently to sound waves. The nerves that relay signals from the inner ear to the brain also degenerate slowly, resulting in various degrees of deafness.

Blue-eyed white cats are usually deaf because of a genetic defect. The specific colour combination of white coat and blue eye is found only in a gene that also produces a defect in one of the structures of the inner ear, resulting in the prevention of the passage of sound waves. If a white cat has only one blue eye, it is deaf in the ear next to the blue eye, but might hear with the other ear.

SIGHT

The cat has large, deep-set eyes that gaze forwards, allowing the field of vision from each eye to overlap and produce a three-dimensional image. Compare this to the rabbit, horse or cow where the eyes are set on either side of the head to give a wide field of vision. The cat, as a result, has a narrower field of vision, but its three-dimensional sight allows it to judge distances accurately when jumping and climbing, or pouncing on prey.

The back of the cat's eye is lined with a mirror-like structure (the tapetum lucidum). This reflects any light not initially absorbed by the retina (where the sight image is formed) and so creates a 'second image'. This greatly increases the cat's visual

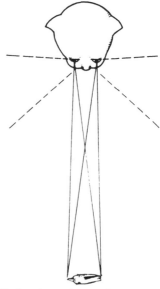

By focusing on its prey the cat can judge its distance and size. The cat's 'peripheral' vision is about 180° and is shown by the dotted lines

sensitivity in dim light. Cats can see in light that is six times dimmer than light in which humans are capable of seeing.

This reflecting shield gave the cat its God-like status in Ancient Egypt. The Egyptians believed that the cat's eyes continued to reflect the sun during the night, so they shaped their God, Ra, in the form of a cat so that Ra could work against the malevolent powers of darkness.

The cat's sight and hunting

The cat needs to see well at night because its main prey are small mammals or rodents, which are most active at night. The cat's eye is acutely sensitive to movement. Once a tiny movement has alerted the cat, it can then concentrate accurately on that spot, sublimating all other movement, such as wind-blown grass.

Q *How does a cat's sight compare with human sight?*

The cat's eye might be more sensitive in dim light than ours, but it lacks the ability to focus and produce a clear, sharp image. It is estimated that our ability to focus is ten times better than the cat's. Sight has evolved as our primary sense. Our ancestors needed close, precise focus for activities such as tool-making. It also enabled them to choose ripe fruits correctly and to avoid poisonous herbs and plants. Acute sight was essential to successful hunting and defence. To the cat, the sense of sight is less important. Their sense of sight is integrated closely with other senses, especially those of hearing and smell. The cat places less reliance on a single sense than we do.

Q *Can cats see colour?*

Tests suggest that cats can differentiate between blue and green, but probably see mainly in shades, much like a colour TV out of tune. Their colour perception is better than that of the dog, but is far less developed than ours.

Q *When does a kitten see properly?*

Kittens are born blind. Their eyes remain closed for the first 7–10 days of life. All kitten's eyes are blue at first, and only gradually mature to reach full development at around three months of age. It is doubtful if kittens see well until they are about six weeks old.

BALANCE

The cat has a remarkable sense of balance, enabling it to perform almost uncanny feats of agility. The cat's sense of sight helps in

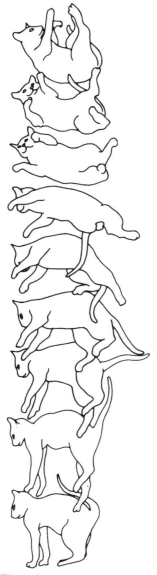

The cat has a remarkable ability to turn itself around to land safely on all four feet

orientation, but the inner ear plays the major role in the cat's balance. Nerves link the ear to a part of the brain called the cerebellum, where information from the inner ear is analysed.

Good balance is essential to cats as they are tree climbers. A well-developed 'righting reflex' protects the cat from injury if it falls. During a fall, the cat extends all four legs, which act like shock absorbers when they hit the ground. The pads on the feet further cushion the force of a fall, reducing the chances of spinal or internal injury.

Cats sometimes make mistakes. A cat is especially liable to misjudge if it is carrying something in its mouth, or it might misjudge the height it is at and make an over-ambitious leap. These errors can result in fractures of the jaw or limbs.

A cat reaches maximum speed of descent after 20 metres; so in theory if a cat can survive a fall of 20 metres it can survive a fall from any height, even from a skyscraper. Survival after falls from enormous heights has been recorded. A cat always has a reasonable chance of survival so long as the fall is on to soft ground.

SMELL

The cat's sense of smell is phenomenal in comparison with our mediocre ability. The cat is able to identify individuals solely by their unique smell, and can detect the presence of this smell long after the person or animal has departed.

Cats possess multiple scent glands that produce a specialised secretion with a persistent, personalised odour. We cannot detect this odour. These scent glands are located on each side of the cat's

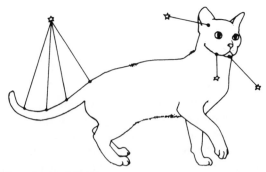

Location of the cat's scent glands

forehead, on the chin and lips and all along the tail. When a cat smooches up and gives you a friendly rub with its head and draws its tail over your legs it is covering you with its scent.

The use of the sense of smell starts from birth. The presence of scents termed 'pheromones' attract the newborn kitten to the mother's nipple. Smell continues to play an important role in eating. Food is always thoroughly sniffed before being accepted. This partly explains why cats are rarely poisoned. They do not rush up and gulp food the way some dogs do. Cats only rarely eat carrion. Most find the smell of tainted food offensive.

If the cat's sense of smell is affected, the result can be catastrophic. During a bout of the flu, congestion of nasal passages causes obstruction of the sense of smell. A severely affected cat usually refuses to eat, or will only be tempted with pungent foods such as cheese or smoked fish. Other habits, such as toilet habits and scent-marking, are also upset. Clearing the nasal passages to restore the sense of smell is a priority in sick cats to hasten recovery.

TASTE

Tastebuds are spaced along the front, edges and base of the tongue. We humans perceive four basic dimensions of taste: sweet, salt, bitter and acid. The cat differs from us in showing little response to 'sweet'. Cats do not rely on taste to the extent that we do. Smell dominates. The cat's sense of taste is at its most acute when the cat is young. As the cat matures, the sense of taste diminishes.

Jacobsen's organ

Another dimension to taste and smell. Cats possess a sensory organ termed the vomeronasal organ, although it is more commonly called Jacobsen's organ (after its discoverer). This provides a third chemical sense in addition to those of taste and smell. It is complementary to both. Jacobsen's organ sits in the roof of the cat's mouth, just behind the incisor teeth. A duct opens from this organ into the mouth. By pressing the tongue up against the duct, odorous chemicals are forced up into the organ.

When the organ is stimulated, the cat extends its neck, opens its mouth and lifts the upper lip. We might be tempted to interpret this as a gesture of disgust, but in the cat it is often closer to ecstasy. Such a reaction is most commonly seen in males responding to the sexually stimulating smells of a queen on heat, when 'turning on' to catnip or when smelling each other's anal regions.

Catnip

The catnip plant (*Nepeta cataria*, also called catmint) emits an odour that is compelling to most cats. Typically, a cat will sniff, then lick or chew the catnip, then stare blankly into space. Perhaps it might shake its head or rub it against the plants, or roll on the ground, purring ecstatically. These episodes last 5–10 minutes and then cannot be repeated for an hour or more.

The catnip's leaves contain an oil called nepetalactone, which is hallocinogenic and is related to marijuana. When the cat presses this oil up into Jacobsen's organ it apparently sends the cat on a mild drug-induced 'trip', hence the space staring and rolling behaviour.

Some manufacturers of cat products utilise the attractiveness of catnip by producing playthings stuffed with catnip leaves or scented with its oil. Up to two-thirds of the cat population are attracted to catnip. Age or sex makes no difference.

However, be warned. If catnip is used excessively it can result in an unpleasant change in the cat's personality.

TOUCH

The cat's foot pads and nose are particularly sensitive to touch. Throw a kitten an unfamiliar toy: first the kitten will reach out with one paw to touch the object lightly, then touch it more firmly. Finally the nose and whiskers are used to make a closer inspection. The cat's nose is quite sensitive to heat. While sniffing at food, cats are also testing the temperature, and they will quickly step back if it is too hot. Cats rarely burn their nose or mouth on hot foods due partly to this heat sensitivity, and partly to their natural caution.

The cat's foot pads are sensitive to touch and to vibrations. Cats will touch their prey to see if it is dead or pat each other or their owners with their pads as an affectionate gesture. They can detect vibrations such as footsteps long before we are aware that someone is approaching. Because of this sensitivity, many cats hate to have their feet touched or stroked. The cat's whiskers are sensitive to stimulations as delicate as air currents. In dim light, the cat relies quite heavily on its whiskers, and can detect objects by their deflection of these air currents. The whiskers also act as a defence for the eyes. When whiskers are touched the cat instinctively blinks.

Most cats love to be stroked and petted, and will brush against legs and nuzzle against other cats or people. The stimulation of stroking has been shown to slow the cat's heart rate, relax the body and increase the rate of digestion in the bowel. The cat's skin is less sensitive to heat than ours is. A cat might sit on a stove too hot for a human to touch, and might even sit near enough to a heater to burn its fur without displaying any apparent discomfort.

THE SIXTH SENSE

Perhaps we don't give cats enough credit. Certainly, they are intelligent and can solve problems, and can then adapt the solution to different problems, for example, opening doors or retrieving a seemingly inaccessible object. Cats will explore and investigate, apparently purely out of curiosity. This is something that less developed or intelligent animals will not.

Sometimes owners wonder how their cat seems to sense when they are depressed, or are going away or are about to get out the flea powder. Cats are acute observers and read our activities, behaviour and routine with surprisingly accurate perception. Some cats choose to ignore a modification in the daily routine. Others are more demonstrative and follow their owner from room to room, refusing to leave them alone, or alternatively dash for cover and refuse to be induced out. This is not ESP. This is achieved by reading and reacting to our behaviour with a surprising sensitivity of observation.

Feline analysis have come up with four major categories of unusual behaviour. For the first three they offer a logical explanation. For the fourth they cannot.

Showing foreknowledge of impending danger or events

As cats are very sensitive to vibrations, felt mainly through the pads of their feet, they can detect minuscule tremors that humans cannot perceive, heralding events such as an earthquake, an eruption or imminent building collapse. They can smell rain or the faint odour of fire along before humans can.

All these sensations are threatening and unfamiliar to the cat, and could trigger quite bizarre behaviour. It is often this unusual behaviour that alerts the owner, and could be a warning that something is amiss.

Foretelling an unexpected return home by the owner

The cat can detect and recognise the familiar vibrations created by such things as the owner's footsteps or the family car. We are usually totally oblivious to these silent vibrations. Reports of cats jumping up to greet their owner up to five minutes before their actual arrival have been attributed to ESP, but is probably only due to the cat's far greater sensitivity to a whole range of stimuli.

Finding a way home after being lost

It is believed that the cat has an acute sense of time as well as a sensitivity to the earth's magnetic field. These sensory perceptions combine and result in the cat's 'biological clock'. The cat senses from the sun's position at a certain time of the day just where it is in relation to its 'home' base, and can therefore tell in which direction home lies.

'Psi-trailing': Locating its owner in an unfamiliar place

There are many accurately recorded cases of that have been left behind when the owners move—sometimes up to hundreds of kilometres away to a new home—and have eventually tracked their owners down. Distances from 20 to 2000 kilometres have been recorded, and one cat took more than two years to reunite itself with its owner.

The explanation for these cases is elusive. Perhaps the cat does have extra-sensory powers.

5 BEHAVIOUR

CATS LIVING WITH CATS

Cats are commonly thought of as solitary animals, preferring to be alone. Certainly while hunting the cat prefers solitude, but contrary to popular belief, most cats can live happily as part of a group. When a number of cats live together, a social structure will be formed within the group with a definite hierarchy, rules and accepted patterns of behaviour.

A basic bond within a group of cats is the mother–kitten relationship. While some males prefer a solitary nomadic role, others become paternal and fit comfortably into a family unit. Within a group, cats will groom, nuzzle and rub against each other, play together and sometimes sleep huddled together. Females will look after one another's kittens and might even feed kittens from other litters.

Social hierarchies are formed. Among females the order is fairly loose, but rank is rigorously observed by the males. The dominant role commands the greatest territory, but, unlike a dog pack leader, he does not necessarily mate with all, or even a majority of, the females.

The order of the male hierarchy is determined by fighting. Whenever a new male arrives, fighting will occur. Several toms must be challenged before ranking is established. Fights are short and vicious but never to the death. Fighting will also occur when a queen comes on heat. The winner does not necessarily enjoy the spoils of victory — the queen decides which tom she will mate with.

Female hierarchy is based mainly on breeding ability. While nursing, a queen enjoys a privileged status and moves up the social scale with each litter. If a female is spayed she will quickly lose her status.

TERRITORIES

Every cat needs its own territory, comprising a home base and a home range. Cats will vigorously defend their territory and comply with a complex code of territorial behaviour, which includes marking out their claim, the establishment of common ground (or neutral areas) and even rules of the road between holdings.

A cat's 'home base' might be no bigger than a sleeping area. In a group, every cat has its own base, which the others respect. The 'home range' comprises sleeping, watching and playing areas as well as hunting runs. The size of the range depends primarily on the availability of food. In domestic cats this factor is controlled, but in feral cats it is critical. Where food is scarce, a range might have to be 20 ha or more. In contrast, many cats can successfully inhabit an area where rodents are plentiful, such as a granary or a

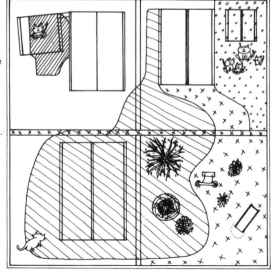

These four blocks of land have been broken up into territories of varying size and shape by three cats.

▨ This neutered male requires only a small territory.
◪ An entire (unneutered) male commands a relatively large area.
▨ A female with kittens will protect her territory aggressively.
▨ Areas are set along which cats can move without enroaching on another's territory and where they can meet on neutral ground.

rubbish dump. Other factors influencing the size of a cat's range include its sex, age and temperament. Older or neutered cats usually have to be content with small territories.

Pathways between territories

Elaborate systems of permissable pathways are developed to allow cats to pass between territories or move to neutral areas, or areas set aside for hunting, mating or as communal meeting grounds. There pathways, although invisible to use, are clear enough to cats. There are definite right-of-way rules on the pathways. Once a cat has entered a pathway it generally has right of way, and even a more dominant cat will await its turn before entering. When two cats meet at an intersection the dominant cat has precedence. The inferior cat has to back off. Fighting can occur, especially if it has been a chance meeting. Surprisingly, females are less tolerant towards one another in these encounters than males.

Territories in households with several cats

Each cat establishes a favourite sleeping area as its home base. Some cats will have more than one of these. In other cases, one cat might hold priority over a particular area during the day but relinquish it to another cat at night.

The home range of a group is generally larger than that held by a single cat. Responsibility for defence of the range is shared by members of the group.

The group also sets aside areas for meetings on a common or neutral ground. The reason for these gatherings is not clear, but they only occur outside the mating season. Cats meeting in these areas can sit close to one another without fear of hostility or aggression. Indeed they will often groom one another.

Moving house

When you move, your cat must establish a new territory. You will already have established your rights by negotiating before moving —presumably without bloodshed. Unfortunately, your cat must fight a way in. The garden of your new house might already 'belong' to another cat. Unneutered males are especially liable to have bloody battles before territorial boundaries are redrawn and they become established in a new domain.

Marking territories

The claimant of any territory must mark out the boundaries. Scent markings are the primary signal, but clearly visible claw scratch marks may also be left on trees or posts.

The scent glands of the cat are located around the lips, temples, tail and anus. When claiming a possession the cat will leave a scent marking on every convenient object, for example, on trees, the legs of furniture, and walls. By rubbing the scent glands of the head against an object, or curling the tail around it by wiping against it with the anal area, the cat deposits a persistent, individualised scent. Other cats will smell the area carefully and might then superimpose their own scent. The urine of male cats contains chemicals termed pheromones, which have a particularly pungent, pervasive odour. When marking an object, the male performs a little ritual. After examining the area he will back up to the object and then accurately spray it with a fine jet of this strongly scented urine. (The male cat's penis points backwards except during an erection.)

Females and castrated males usually do not spray urine, but might do so if they feel stressed or threatened, for example, after moving to a new house or when a cat moves in to threaten his or her territory.

The urine of a queen on heat also contains pheromones. This is a signal to males that she is on heat and available for mating. This scent message is not territorial marking. The queen will usually urinate at ground level rather than spraying walls and trees.

SCRATCHING

Cats scratch trees and posts for two reasons. One is to mark territory, the other is to keep their claws sharp by removing loose scales. The ritual of claw-sharpening is part of the cat's body language and can also be used to intimidate watching cats.

When a cat scratches an object, scent from glands in the foot pads are also deposited. Males will usually reinforce this smell by also spraying the scratched object with urine.

Claw-sharpening can be a big problem if it is misdirected on to valuable furniture or walls. If you intend a cat to live inside it is prudent to accustom it early in life to a scratching post. This is a standing post mounted on a solid, heavy base and covered with fabric, bark or carpet. To introduce a kitten to the post, sit in front of the post, place its front feet on the material and gently mimic a scratching action with its paws.

Once a cat has developed the habit of scratching furniture, it is difficult to break the habit, but one of the following procedures might work:

- Place the scratching post near the damaged furniture or wall. Spray the objects to be protected with a cat repellent spray (available from vets or pet shops) or use a strongly scented polish or similar. Do *not* use any product containing ammonia as this could exacerbate the marking behaviour.

- Trimming the cat's nails yourself might suffice. This is not hard to do if the cat cooperates. Ask your vet to show you how much nail to clip off if you are uncertain.

- Declawing cats (that is, removing the entire nail surgically) is advocated by some. This should only be comtemplated if the cat is exclusively indoors, otherwise it needs the claws for climbing and for defence. The attitude to declawing varies between vets and from country to country. If you wish to have your cat declawed talk it over with your vet first—it might not be necessary.

A scratching post can save furniture

HUNTING

The cat is an excellent hunter adapted to catching small rodents but also capable of successfully hunting other prey, such as birds, snakes, frogs or even fish, depending on their territory. It was the cat's hunting prowess that first led to its domestication as a ratter.

Cats are solitary hunters. Patient, observant and intelligent, they are capable of planning a hunt, locating their prey with senses tuned to detect the slightest movement or smell and then exercising enormous patience waiting for their prey to make the wrong move that provides them with an opening. Cats have been known to sit for days waiting for their quarry to emerge from cover.

Training for hunting starts at about 4–6 weeks of age. The cat has strong, inherited hunting instincts, but if it does not receive instruction in hunting by the time it is about 4–5 months old, it might never learn to hunt or will do so only laboriously.

The mother first introduces the kittens to hunting by bringing them dead prey. When the kittens become accustomed to this, and have commenced playing games, she will bring live prey. Hunting instincts and efficiency are refined and polished by accompanying the mother on hunting expeditions.

The cats' habit of toying with their prey might be repulsive to us, but this seemingly cruel behaviour is necessary to hone their hunting reflexes and techniques. Some believe it is an avenue of tension release.

Q *Can I stop my cat killing birds?*

Many cat owners are extremely unhappy about their cat killing birds. Others refuse to have a cat because of this tendency. The cat's hunting instinct is deep-rooted. Once a cat has learned to kill it is difficult to deflect this drive. The best way to tackle this problem is to prevent the kitten from learning to hunt. If the mother is not a hunter you will probably have little trouble. If she is, you should try to eliminate any access to prey. This means keeping her locked in at night, or preventing her from getting back to the kittens with the fruits of her hunt. This could be quite simply achieved by locking her out and letting her back in with the kittens only after you have removed any trophy she is returning with. If the kittens are not exposed to hunting training, there is a good chance that they will not realise their hunting potential.

Once the cat has learned to hunt, your aim is to try to break the habit or try to protect the birds. Attaching a bell or, better still, *two* bells, to the cat's collar might help to alert the birds, although usually the cat will learn to move without jangling the bells.

Aversion techniques might succeed. An old-fashioned idea that occasionally works is to tie a dead victim to the cat's collar, but this can be aesthetically unpleasant. Another is to set up the cat. This takes some planning and effort. Your aim is to get the cat to associate hunting with an unpleasant sensation. As the cat is stalking a bird, the owner waits for the penultimate moment, then shoots a jet of water at the cat. Something equally startling or unpleasant, such as letting off a cracker or firing pistol blanks, could be used instead of the jet of water. It might be necessary to repeat this procedure many times before it takes effect. Do not let the cat see you doing the squirting or similar. It must associate the unpleasantness with the activity, not with you.

To give the birds a better chance, make sure any bird feeding areas or nesting boxes are sited in open areas where the cat cannot use cover to approach or lie in wait.

Q *Why do some cats bring home birds or mice? Are they showing off?*

These cats are probably expressing a concern for their owner's well-being rather than showing off or looking for praise. This behaviour is presumably a modification of the natural instinct of a mother to bring back food to the nest. It does not warrant punishment, which would only confuse the cat. If you don't want to encourage these small presents it is best to make no response at all, either negative or positive. Ignore the cat if you can, and dispose of the body when the cat is not observing you.

Q *Do cats make better mousers if they are starved?*

Surprisingly, cats are more efficient mousers if they are fed properly. The explanation offered is that the well-fed cat lacks any element of anxiety about food and is more clinically efficient in the kill.

BODY LANGUAGE

Body postures, positions and actions are fundamental methods of communicating between cats. Together with facial expressions and vocalisation, a cat can accurately convey its feelings to other cats. We can learn a lot about our cat if we understand a little of this body language.

Contentment

Body posture and facial expressions are very important in communicating different moods. A contented cat will have relaxed muscles and erect perky ears, and might groom itself with long slow licks. Pleasure at seeing its owner is indicated by the cat standing with the head lowered, hindquarters raised and tail held up straight. The tip of the tail is usually bent slightly forward and wavers slowly from side to side. In this case the cat rises and approaches slightly stiff-legged. It then rubs its cheeks, chin and whiskers against the owner's legs, often winding the tail around simultaneously. The cat might also purr and make rhythmic kneading motions with its feet (see the following section on vocalisation). When the cat is being petted the eyelids become half closed, the third eyelid might slip partially across the eye, the whiskers are relaxed and the ears erect.

If the cat is greeting another friendly cat, sniffing around the head, nose-touching and anal gland-sniffing are usually seen. This is sometimes followed by mutual grooming. Individuals are recognised by scent, and the areas sniffed are where the scent glands are concentrated. Very friendly cats rub against each other, scent-marking their companion with their own smell for future recognition. Pet cats rub against their owners for the same reason.

An alert cat has a direct gaze with forward-pointing ears and whiskers. The nostrils might quiver slightly as the cat tries to identify

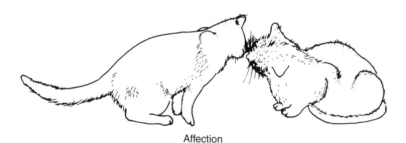

Affection

and recognise an intruder by smell as well as by sight and sound. If the cat senses a threat from a stranger it will freeze, all its muscles tensing. The pupils are constricted (into slits), and the cat will attempt to stare out the opponent. As the stranger approaches, the stance changes. The tip of the elevated tail points down, the chin is drawn in (to protect its throat), the ears flatten, and the cat turns slowly to one side so it looks larger and more threatening. Gradually the hairs along the tail and body are erected. This is an aggressive posture in which the cat is trying to look as intimidating as possible. The hindlegs are tensed and ready to spring in attack or flight. The weight of the front of the body is supported on one foreleg while the other is prepared to

Fear — threat

Fear — submission

strike. The lips might be drawn back so that the teeth are displayed in a snarl and the cat growls fiercely. The pupils remain as slits, and the tail wags aggressively from side to side. If the unwelcome visitor backs away, the cat might move forward smacking its lips, salivating and growling. When the threat has gone the cat will sniff at the invaded ground and then might spray urine, defaecate or claw at the ground before regaining its normal appearance and composure.

Fighting might occur, especially if two males are involved. Fighting is normally ritualised to bites and claw rakes being directed towards the shoulder and neck region. These areas are protected in the non-castrated male by thickened skin. The cheeks of the tom cat give him a fuller face, which help in display. The bigger-looking the face, the more intimidating it would be to a rival. This is also why the lynx has fat cheeks and the lion has a mane.

When a cat is anxious or afraid the pupils dilate, the eyes dart rapidly from side to side looking for an escape route. It might adopt a submissive position crouching, with ears and whiskers flattened on its head. Cats don't urinate in submission as dogs sometimes do. Submission could have the effect of appeasement if the aggressor is another

Submission

cat who then withdraws without attacking. If the aggressor approaches, the cat might roll on its back, but a paw will be raised and be used to defend itself if the need arises. Alternatively, if a frightened cat can see an escape route, it will flee. If the cat is cornered, it could become defensive (a combination of fear and aggression). The cat growls,

Aggression

hisses and spits. The back is arched, and the cat stands side on to make it look larger and more threatening. Ultimately such a cat will attack if the stranger approaches to a distance less than a metre away. At this point the cat can no longer flee, so self-defence is the only option.

A sick or wretched cat has a miserable facial expression, the tail is low, and it spends a good deal of time hunched up, often not bothering to eat or wash.

Cats in an agony of indecision about how to behave in a perplexing or frightening situation might start to groom themselves in so-called displacement activity. (Compare a human biting fingernails.)

Cats have a dislike of being looked at directly. If a cat being secretly observed suddenly becomes aware of the fact, it will stop whatever it is doing and then resume its activities in an obviously self-conscious and more hesitant manner.

VOCALISATION

Cats don't actually form words, but they do appear to possess quite a vocabulary of meaningful sounds. Scientists have detected sixteen distinctive vocal sounds and believe there are many others that are inaudible to people. Some breeds are more vocal than others. Siamese are especially so, while Abyssinians tend to be quiet, but all cats are capable of a range of sounds. Many owners learn to tell from their cat's distinctive miaowing sounds whether it is happy or hungry, complaining, bewildered or just seeking attention. Cats can change the inflection to demand or merely to request. These different sound are clear enough to an observant owner. Communication by sound between cats is probably much more extensive and subtle than we can appreciate.

Other distinct sounds we recognise in cats include the high-pitched mating yowl of the female on heat and the distinct call of the sexually excited tom. The queen miaows, cries, chirrups and croons to her kittens. They respond appropriately to these different calling signals.

Purring

Cats are able to purr from the age of about a week. They purr while sucking on a teat, pausing only to swallow. Purring is usually a sign of well-being and contentment, although an injured or frightened cat might purr loudly, perhaps as a pleading gesture.

All cats purr. Some purr for hours, self-inducing a euphoric state. Perhaps this is a regression to kittenhood as some cats not only purr but also make all the other motions of suckling at a teat and salivate while sucking and pawing at the imaginary mammary gland.

Kittens purr only in a monotone. Adults can purr very softly or build up to a loud vibrant roar. Veterinary surgeons attempting to listen with a stethescope to the cat's chest are frequently frustrated because all that can be heard is a deep purring as the cat lies between the owner's hands. But purring can also work to a vet's advantage. In a patient suffering from breathing difficulties, for example, in a case of cat flu, if the cat can be induced to purr, then the breathing is greatly eased and the cat usually becomes more settled and comfortable.

Q *How do cats purr?*

We do not know for certain how cats purr. The most popular theory is that the purr is produced by a rhythmic vibration of the cat's vocal cords. These are situated in the larynx, at the entrance to the windpipe at the back of the cat's mouth. An electrical impulse flows through a nerve to stimulate the vocal cords briefly to contract. After a fractional pause, this electrical impulse is repeated. This causes the vocal cords alternatively to open and close as often as twenty or thirty times a second. The resultant intermittent air pressure changes in the larynx result in a purring sound.

SLEEPING

Cats spend about two-thirds of their life in sleep. The actual number of hours each day varies with circumstances, such as the weather or whether the cat is hungry. During the mating season, toms finds it difficult to relax at all and get very little sleep.

Cats do not have the same sleeping manners as people. We can sleep a solid eight hours. The cat spends more than half its day in a state called 'light sleep' or 'catnapping'. In light sleep, many of the cat's senses remain on guard. Hearing is especially acute, and the body muscles are only incompletely relaxed. The cat can revert virtually instantly to full alert. Catnaps usually last 10–30 minutes.

In 'deep sleep' the cat relaxes its body and muscles. Its senses are depressed and reactions slowed. The cat only needs 3–4 hours of this type of sleep per day. It is probable that cats dream during sleep as they have periods of rapid eye movement, a state associated with dreaming in humans. During these periods their ears, paws and nose will often twitch and tremble, and the cat might paw and scratch at phantom objects.

As cats get older they spend more time in deep sleep, and this muscle-twitching and jerking can be quite dramatic. This worries some owners, but it appears to be perfectly normal.

Kittens younger than a month old only have two speeds: stop or flat out. They indulge in deep sleep only. The state of light sleep is learned later.

BEHAVIOUR PROBLEMS

When you consider how much we have subjected cats to demands that they conform with our pattern of life, it is not surprising that we encounter behavioural problems. We have taken away their need to hunt by providing food. We prevent them from breeding by locking them up or neutering them, or we go so far as to select for them what we consider a good breeding partner. We pamper, cosset and protect them. Domestication has brought great benefits to cats. Their expected life span has increased enormously. The life span of the wild male averages only three years. Wild females live only about a year longer.

By sublimating many of the cat's natural instincts and trying to curb those we perceive as undesirable, such as sharpening the claws, we have put new stresses on them. Sometimes this results in activities we label as 'problem' or 'nuisance' behaviour.

Aggressive behaviour in cats

Some aggression in cats is a natural and normal part of their inherited behaviour patterns. Cats will defend territory and protect their young, their food or themselves if they feel threatened. Some cats have an excessive tendency to aggression and become a problem

for other animals or humans. Fights between
cats are best left for the cats to work out.
These fights are often necessary to
establish a decision over a territorial
dispute or a place in the cat hierarchy.
Attacks on humans might occur over
food. If a cat threatens or attacks you
around mealtime it is essential not
to feed the cat until it has settled
down again. Feeding too soon after
aggressive behaviour might only
reinforce it. In reprimanding an
aggressive cat, do not indulge in physical hurt. A firm command 'NO!'
backed up by a flick to the cat's nose is
usually enough. If you attempt to slap or
smack your cat you could end up badly scratched.

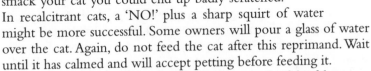

In recalcitrant cats, a 'NO!' plus a sharp squirt of water
might be more successful. Some owners will pour a glass of water
over the cat. Again, do not feed the cat after this reprimand. Wait
until it has calmed and will accept petting before feeding it.

Some cats are not so much aggressive as fearful of humans.
Their behaviour is only self-protective. Solving this problem
requires patience and time to gain their trust. Some people have an
affinity with cats and can win almost any cat over, but some cats
will never be tamed.

Q *After I have been stroking my cat it suddenly attacks me. Why?*

Worried owners sometimes report that their cat seems to have a
'Jekyll and Hyde' personality. One moment it is lying docile being
stroked and petted, and the next it flies into an apparent rage,
scratching and hissing, then fleeing from the owner. This behaviour
occurs usually when it is the underbelly or chest that is stroked. In
the wild, the at adopts a submissive posture by lying on its back,
showing neck and underbelly to the dominant cat. In these cats,
stroking might stimulate the sensation of being attacked and trigger a reflex 'fight and flight' response, where the cat lashes out at
the apparent threat, then bolts for safety.

Beware of the cat that is already frightened—perhaps by a
thunderstorm, an unexpected loud noise or the presence of an
unfamiliar dog. If the owner attempts to pick this cat up, or even
stroke it, the state of tension might induce the cat to react aggressively. It is better to talk to the cat. Let it relax before attempting

anything further. Certainly such reflex self-protection behaviour does not warrant punishment.

MOVING HOUSE

While a dog becomes primarily attached to people and is happy to go wherever they do, cats are often more concerned about territories. Consequently, moving house can be quite traumatic for a cat. The cat usually becomes unsettled long before the actual move because of the atmosphere of discord and turmoil around it. It is common for owners to be unable to find their cat when the time comes finally to transport it to the new house. A prudent move might be to lock the cat in a spare room the night before the move, or even board it at a cattery for a few days.

On arrival at your new home keep the cat indoors for at least 48 hours. Then let it out only under supervision. Give it as many familiar items as you can, such as bedding, favourite toys or even a chair it is fond of. Keep the same litter trays, feeding bowls and scratching post. The fewer changes, the better at this stage.

Give as much assurance as you can. Some signs of anxiety should be expected, for example, refusing to eat, becoming moody or hiding away. Some will temporarily start to defaecate or urinate inappropriately in the new home.

Drugs might help in some cases. Tranquillisers might be useful for the nervous traveller or very excitable cat. These are only available through your vet. Other medications your vet might discuss include megoestrol acetate, a hormone that apparently induces a feeling of well-being or euphoria in some cats, allowing them to adjust much faster and more smoothly to an otherwise traumatic change.

Many owners have tried the old trick of putting butter on the cat's paws when it arrives in the new house. The idea is that, by the time the cat has finished licking the butter out of its paws, it will have adjusted to its new surroundings. Whether this works or not we are not sure, but many of our clients swear by it.

WOOL-SUCKING

Some cats love to suck, lick or chew. What at first seems an amusing habit can develop into a real problem for both the cat and its owner.

Why do these cats suck wool? The reason is obscure, although in some Siamese there is a strong inherited tendency. Perhaps some cats like the taste of the lanolin in the wool. In others the wool-sucking is probably a displaced suckling drive, similar to thumb-sucking in children. The odour of lanolin resembles the odour given off from the mother's nipple when she is nursing. This might account for the typical wool-sucker's behaviour. Some of these cats induce in themselves an almost trance-like state, their eyes gazing over as they suck or chew, simultaneously kneading with their forepaws at a phantom breast. Wool-suckers can not only cause serious damage to expensive carpets or clothes but also induce in themselves gastric upsets or even intestinal blockages.

Controlling this behaviour is difficult and sometimes impossible. Try dusting the woollen object with pepper. Covering the object with a scent that is unattractive to the cat might break the habit. Try carpet deodorant preparations or strong scents such as lavender. Naphthalene could be effective, but is less pleasant to have around. For example, stick moth balls to wallpaper or furniture. Not very decorative, but often effective! Restrict access to wool as much as practicable. This helps, but the behaviour might return if wool is re-encountered in the future.

As wool-sucking can be an inherited trait it is unwise to get a kitten from a litter where one of the parents is a known wool-sucker.

EMOTIONAL UPSETS

The two most common signs of an upset cat are loss of appetite and changes in toilet habits. They might start urinating or defaecating in the house. The cause of the upset might not be obvious. It could be due to something we are not aware of or to something that doesn't disturb us at all. Some of the more common causes of behavioural or emotional upset are:

- New cat in the neighbourhood, such as one of the family moving out or a new baby arriving.
- A new dog or other pet.
- Abnormal activities in or around the house, such as roadworks outside, a plumber calling or redecoration.
- Thunderstorms.
- A cat comes into heat nearby.

The reason for the upset is often not immediately apparent. Most of the factors listed above wouldn't disturb ourselves but could be quite distressing for the cat. Some cats are fairly tolerant of these stresses, others might be severely affected.

Treatment

The best solution is to discover and eliminate the cause. This is often not possible or practicable. In time, many cats readjust and no specific treatment is necessary. Tranquillisers can be used in the short term but are not a long-term solution. Drugs such as meg-oestrol acetate (Ovarid, Ovoban etc.) can be used by a vet to help the cat if it is seriously upset. If the appetite remains jaded, try vit-amin B supplements, or offer foods with a strong smell such as fish.

Q *My cat occasionally runs madly round the house. Is this some form of fit?*

No. Such behaviour is considered normal. Some cats do it fre-quently, perhaps even daily at around the same time. Individuals vary as to their exact behaviour, but a typical episode would be as follows: the cat suddenly fixes its gaze on a phantom object, then races madly around the house in apparent pursuit.

One possible explanation links this behaviour to the cat's hunt-ing instincts, which can be very strong. If not released in the natural manner, the cat is driven to release the pent-up nervous energy in pursuit of fantasy prey.

Q *Why does my cat groom itself after being told off?*

In times of embarrassment, humans blush or become confused. Some people will loosen their collar or adjust their clothing, perhaps pull on a shirt sleeve or brush imaginary dust from a lapel. This serves to cover embarrass-ment. We believe the cat is doing the same when it sits down and starts to groom itself immedi-ately after being chastised.

Similarly, some cats overgroom if subjected to uncomfortable or stressful situations, such as moving house or if another cat is introduced into the home.

Q *My cat behaves abominably if left home by itself. Why?*

Although most cats are independent and enjoy periods of solitude, others seem to crave company. This is especially common with orphan kittens that have been hand-reared and consequently have become overdependent on human contact. When left alone they fret and might become destructive or exhibit neurotic behaviour, such as urinating on the carpet. Others simply become bored with long periods of isolation, especially if they are in a restricted area, such as an apartment.

A common expression of boredom or stress is for the cat to groom itself excessively or begin self-sucking. This can lead to other problems such as skin damage. The licking or sucking inflames the skin, exciting the sensory nerves in the skin's surface. In time, a vicious cycle can establish itself as the licking causes the skin to be extremely itchy: lick—itch—lick—itch. The cat eventually cannot leave itself alone. The most commonly damaged areas are the tail tip, the paws and the skin over the wrist and hock.

Other expressions of boredom or resentment include tearing curtains, uprooting plants or pulling all the washing out of the basket.

The following measures might help to reduce or even eliminate this behaviour:

- Feed the cat just before you leave rather than routinely when you arrive home.
- Leave the cat plenty of toys to play with.
- Allow the cat a window to look out of. Don't close all the blinds. If you leave only one blind up, select one where the cat gets a little sun.
- A radio left playing can fill the void. Select a station playing restrained music. Frenzied rock music does not have the desired soothing effect—this has been proved.
- A companion animal might help, although this is unpredictable. Getting two kittens initially rather than one can prevent the problem arising. Introducing a new cat is risky as your cat may not accept the newcomer. The cat most likely to be accepted is a kitten of the opposite sex to the problem cat.

6 NUTRITION

Cats are true carnivores. Their natural food is small rodents. Cats require high levels of animal protein and some animal fats in their diet. Unlike dogs, they cannot survive on substitutes of vegetable origin, such as soy bean meal. Cats do not consume much of the intestinal and stomach contents of their prey, nor, in their natural state, do they eat other vegetables or cereals to supplement their diet. Because there are certain elements cats must have that can only be supplied from animal flesh it is not possible to raise a cat as a vegetarian.

The cat eats only until energy requirements have been met. This is, on average, 250 to 280 kilocalories (kcal) a day for an adult cat. If the diet is well structured, or what nutritionalists term 'balanced', then by the time the cat has consumed 250 kcal it will have also consumed its daily requirements of protein, vitamins, minerals and fats. Unfortunately, many diets are not well balanced. If fed an unbalanced diet, the cat might consume its required energy needs and therefore stop eating before it has met its protein (and other) requirements. Diets excessively rich in fats and carbohydrates can therefore lead to protein deficiencies.

The majority of cats eat only to sustain themselves and not for pleasure. Although they have a reputation for being finicky and choosy, it is more accurate to say that cats are very careful about what they eat. Some cats do become fussy. If you indulge your cat and pander to its every whim, you are liable to find it difficult or even impossible to change the diet if the need arises.

BEWARE! Cats can become virtually addicted to certain foods, such as liver or meat.

It is essential to train your cat to eat a variety of foods right from the start. If a cat is allowed to eat nothing but liver or meat or a similarly non-balanced diet, it will eventually develop serious nutritional deficiency diseases. It is frustrating to have to treat these cats because, although the vet knows that the solution is to correct the diet, the cat might refuse any alternative to its habitual fare.

WHAT YOU SHOULD FEED YOUR CAT

You might choose to base your cat's diet on good-quality commercial foods, or you might prefer to prepare the cat's meals yourself. Many owners choose to do a bit of both. The aim is to provide all the cat's nutritional requirements, avoiding deficiencies or gross excess. A 'balanced' diet is formulated so that when a cat has eaten enough of the diet to satisfy its energy requirements, and therefore its hunger, it will also have consumed enough of all other required nutrients: vitamins, minerals, trace elements, protein, fats and carbohydrates.

Commercial foods

In most countries, pet food manufacturers are forbidden by law to misrepresent their product on the label. In other words, they cannot make false claims regarding their product's content. So if you read the packet label, it can tell you quite a lot.

Here are a few descriptive terms used by cat food manufacturers. Some commonly used terms include:

- *Complete*: This term means that this food supplies all the nutrients required by a cat, including protein, fats, vitamins, minerals and trace elements.
- *Incomplete*: (Most foods fall into this category.) These foods do not meet all of the cat's nutritional requirements, and should therefore not be fed as the sole food, even though the cat likes them, or because they are readily available or inexpensive.

- *Varietal*: A commercial food intended to provide variety in the cat's diet, but not formulated to be used as a staple food. Examples include sardines, pilchards in aspic and rabbit pieces. These varietals are usually highly palatable. Cats love them. Beware of letting the cat become too dependent on them—they are 'incomplete' foods.
- *Treats*: These are foods used as snacks or rewards. They might have little nutritional value but are always designed to be highly attractive. Examples include 'fishy treats'. They should be used as intended: as treats only, and not as an integral part of the diet.

Feed your cat a variety of food types, brands and flavours.

ESSENTIAL COMPONENTS OF A CAT'S DIET

If you choose to prepare your cat's meals yourself, you should know the essential components of a cat's diet.

Protein

The cat has an extraordinarily high requirement for protein (e.g. eggs, meat, milk, fish, soy bean, yeast). Its diet must contain 34%–40% protein. In fact, the cat might refuse to eat a diet containing less than 20% protein. As an indication of just how much more protein cats require in comparison to other species, it has been calculated that kittens require about two and a half times the levels of protein required by puppies, while adult cats require nearly five times the amount required by adult dogs. A kitten could starve on dog food.

There are some essential dietary components that the cat cannot manufacture itself and which are only supplied in animal protein, for example, the amino acid taurine. This is not the case in dogs or humans. Cats cannot survive on vegetable protein alone. (Dogs and humans can.)

Sources of protein and how to prepare them

Eggs are better served cooked than raw. The white of the egg is more easily digested by the cat when cooked. Raw egg white con-

tains avidin, which interferes with
the essential B vitamin biotin.
Avidin is destroyed by heat. Meat
can be fed raw or cooked, although
cats could pick up tapeworm infestation, toxoplasmosis and other conditions
from raw meat. From a public health
viewpoint, it is preferable to cook the meat.

Fish and fish meals are an excellent, palatable source of protein, but beware of feeding raw
fish to excess. Diets comprising more than 10% raw fish can
become thiamine deficient (thiamine is an essential B vitamin). This
is because some raw fish contain the enzyme thiaminase, which
destroys this vitamin, and a condition termed Chastek's paralysis
could result. This condition used to be seen quite commonly in cats
living in fishing communities. (See chapter 18 on nerves.)

Milk is an excellent source of protein plus calcium, phospho-
rous and various other minerals and vitamins. Unfortunately,
some cats are intolerant of milk sugars, while others are allergic
to the milk protein. Cow's milk can be a useful part of the cat's
diet, but it is not essential. Some owners become concerned
because their kitten will not drink milk. This is not necessary—
cow's milk is no more a natural food for cats than cheese is for
mice. There are plenty of other foods that supply all the nutrients
contained in milk.

Fats

Cats must have some animal fats in their diet. They cannot survive
on vegetable-based substitutes. Cats deprived of animal fats have
poor growth rates, a harsh, dry coat, skin ulcers and sores. They are
highly susceptible to disease and are usually infertile. The essential
nutrients contained in fats are technically known as essential fatty
acids. Most animals can manufacture all their own essential fatty
acids, but the cat cannot.

Fats are a concentrated source of energy. A unit of fat contains
double the calorie value of the same weight of protein. Fat is rich
in vitamins A, D, E and K.

Cats can cope with a high level of fat in their diet. Like all other
foods, the fat must be broken down in the digestive tract into its basic
components before it can be absorbed into the body. It is a common
misconception that if a cat is fed fat it will become fat. This is not so,
unless you feed too much. Instead of trimming all the fat off the cat's
meat, it is better to leave it on and simply don't give so much.

Used cooking fat should never be given to cats. It is likely to contain peroxides, which are toxic to cats.

Unsaturated fatty acids

Some types of fat contain excessive amounts of components termed unsaturated fatty acids or UFAs. There is a condition variously called yellow fat disease, steatitis or pansteatitis, which results from feeding cats excessive amounts of food containing UFAs, such as fish oils. Signs of yellow fat disease are hard, painful lumps, which form in the fat deposits under the cat's skin. The cat becomes feverish, loses all appetite and becomes reluctant to move and extremely sensitive to touch. The treatment is to change the cat's diet and give it high supplements of vitamin E.

Carbohydrates

Cats do not need carbohydrates provided that their diet contains enough protein and fat to satisfy their energy requirements. Nevertheless, carbohydrates can be a useful part of the cat's diet. Cats can use the carbohydrate as an energy source, thereby 'sparing' protein, which can be used instead for tissue building and repair.

Sources of carbohydrates include sugars, cereals, potatoes, pasta and rice. Cats can digest most carbohydrates more readily if they are cooked. They cannot digest cellulose, which is the carbohydrate that forms plant cell walls. These plant fibres are still a useful component of the cat's diet as they act as a 'bulking' agent and can help the cat to form proper stools.

Carbohydrates can comprise up to a third of the cat's diet provided adequate levels of fat and protein are also present. If there is too high a level of carbohydrate, the cat will stop eating before all its essential daily protein and fat requirements have been met, because cats only eat until their energy requirements are satisfied.

Do not feed your cat milk or cream. Some commercially prepared modified milk products are safe to feed.

Milk is the single most common cause of diarrhoea in kittens.

Water

Water is essential for life. If a cat is deprived of both food and water, it is dehydration that kills. If your cat stops eating for a few days it might become dehydrated and you might have to force it to drink fluids. Food is important, but it is not as critical as water. The amount of water any cat needs daily depends on a lot of factors, including the ambient temperature, amount of exercise, nutritional state and so on. A very rough estimate of need is 50 ml per kg of body weight per day.

Most of the cat's daily water comes from the food. In many cases, cats extract all their daily requirements from their food. The feline kidneys are extremely efficient at retaining fluid, so the cat does not lose as much fluid in the urine as most species do. Inevitably, some water is lost as the cat must flush away the normal waste products of body metabolism. Cats that are fed dry or semi-moist foods *do* require additional water.

The easiest approach to water intake is simply to have plenty of clean water available at all times. Let the cat drink as much as it likes when it likes.

Vegetables

Vegetables are not a natural food source for cats. Cats can only digest them after they have been cooked, and even then many cats refuse to eat them, presumably because they don't like the smell or taste. Small amounts of cooked vegetables mixed with the rest of the cat's food are useful additional sources of vitamins and minerals.

Vitamins and minerals

Cats can synthesise most of their own vitamins, with the exception of vitamin A and niacin, both of which must be supplied in their diet. Many minerals must be supplied in the cat's diet. Supplements specifically formulated for cats are available. They are rarely required in normal cats with good dietary variety.

Q   *What should I feed my cat?*

The golden rule is to vary the foods you give. If you feed a variety of good-quality commercial cat foods your cat should thrive. Home recipes are liable to be deficient in some of the essential dietary elements. Snacks and treats should not form a major part of your cat's diet, although most cats enjoy and benefit from such treats, for example drinks of milk, scraps of meat and 'fishy treats'.

Table 3: Minerals and their characteristics

Mineral	Source	Function	Deficiency	Excess
Vitamin A	Fish oils, liver, egg yolk, milk fat, kidneys.	Vision in dim light. Maintains skin.	Night blindness, skin sores, behavioural changes, decreased reproductive performance.	Loss of appetite, pain on handling, bone malformation.
Thiamin (Vit. B1)	Dairy products, brewer's yeast, organ meats.	Release of energy from carbohydrate.	Anorexia, vomiting, paralysis, ventroflexion of head.	

Q   *How often should I feed my cat?*

Cats prefer to eat a little at a time. They prefer several small meals to one or larger meals. Adult cats should be fed at least twice daily. Kittens should be fed 3–6 times daily. Cats eat to satisfy their energy needs. When the cat has consumed enough to supply this energy requirement it will stop eating. If the diet is correctly balanced it will by this time have also consumed enough protein, fat, vitamins and minerals to meet its daily needs.

Ad-lib feeding, or free access to food, is a feeding method that works well with most cats. Some will become obese, but the majority of cats regulate themselves well. It is usually the cat confined indoors that becomes overweight as there is little opportunity or stimulus to exercise and therefore burn energy.

Q   *Exactly how much should I feed my cat?*

There is no simple answer. The cat's needs vary with all sorts of factors, such as age, the climate, amount of exercise and many other individual factors. A growing kitten requires 200–500 kcal per day and an average adult around 300–350 kcal per day. However, the variation is enormous, and it should be taken as a starting point only and varied with individual results.

Q   *Should I give my pregnant queen more food?*

Queens do not require any special feeding during pregnancy. It is during lactation that they need more food. Read chapter 7 on 'Reproduction' for more information.

Q   *Can feeding liver cause any problems?*

A little liver makes an excellent contribution to the cat's diet, but too much can be harmful. Liver is so palatable that some cats become virtually addicted to it, and these cats will eventually develop problems. The major risk in feeding too much liver is that it contains excessive amounts of vitamin A, which is stored by the body and could gradually build up to a toxic level. One to two tablespoons per week is enough.

The first sign of vitamin A poisoning is usually that the cat has difficulty grooming. This is because, under the influence of excess vitamin A, changes are occuring in the spine, making it less flexible. The spinal ligaments, which are normally quite elastic, gradually become mineralised

Vitamin A poisoning

and hard. Movement of the spine becomes painful, and eventually impossible. If this condition is detected early, treatment can be effective, but in many cases the condition is irreversible.

Q *My cat loves meat and won't eat anything else. Is this all right?*

No. Meat alone is not enough. Meat does not contain enough calcium, iron, iodine, sodium, copper or magnesium. Kittens brought up on meat alone have poor bone development and growth. The bones bow, are fragile and easily fractured. The kitten might be weak and uncoordinated. This condition is seen in all types of cats, although Siamese seem to be particularly prone. Perhaps this is because they can become finicky eaters if allowed to get away with it early.

Q *Should the cat's food be served warm?*

Cats seem to prefer foods to be served at blood temperature. Palatability is reduced if the food is served straight out of the refrigerator.

Q *My cat likes dog food. Is there any harm in feeding it?*

Small amounts of dog food are all right. It will certainly not cause it to start barking, but dog foods are not a suitable base for a cat's diet. They do not contain enough protein, and the balance of nutrients is not correct for a cat's requirements. A kitten could starve if given only dog food.

7 REPRODUCTION

The sexual behaviour of cats is so vastly different from human sexual behaviour that comparisons can lead to confusion. While it is a natural inclination to interpret our pet's behaviour in terms of our emotions or experience, such comparisons are not valid. Many of the problems that cat owners encounter stem from a failure to appreciate this point.

Here are some terms used in this chapter:
- *Queen*—a breeding female.
- *Stud*—a breeding male.
- *Tom*—a male cat. The useage of *tom* is fairly loose and is sometimes applied to neutered males as well as entire males.
- *Heat*—that phase of the female's sexual cycle when she is attractive to the stud and will mate.
- *In season*—synonym for being on heat.
- *On call*—synonym for being on heat.
- *Queening*—giving birth to kittens.
- A *castrate*—desexed male cat.

- A *neuter*—desexed male or female cat.
- *Entire*—not neutered.

TO BREED OR NOT TO BREED?

Domestic cats are extremely fertile. They reach puberty early and have a long breeding life. Queens can produce and rear up to three litters a year. This results in far too many kittens being born for the homes available. Animal welfare organisations are faced with the melancholy task of destroying a surprising number of cats every week. Up to 80% of all stray cats entering shelters have to be euthanised despite vigorous efforts to find them homes. A cat population explosion can occur with alarming speed. Before you breed, be certain you have homes for the kittens.

Several misconceptions regarding breeding could unfortunately lead to owners allowing their cats to have litters unnecessarily. For example, it might be thought that the experience of coming into heat or of having a litter will improve the cat's personality and character. This is not so. Having a litter has no long-term effect. Sometimes owners wish to allow their cat to have kittens so that the children can have the experience of watching birth. This is certainly a moving and worthwhile experience, but there are alternatives. In most cases, the queen prefers solitude, and the birth often occurs in the early morning, so for either or both of these reasons, the children might miss the event. It is usually possible instead to arrange a viewing of a breeder's queen giving birth, or of a friend's bitch whelping, or even of a mare foaling or a cow calving.

In summary, unless you have an excellent reason for breeding, have your cat desexed.

PREVENTING PREGNANCY

The available methods of preventing pregnancy are:
- Surgery: The most common method of preventing pregnancy is to spay the female. This means the surgical removal of the reproductive organs.
- Drugs: In some countries there are drugs available to prevent the queen from coming into heat or to stop heat once it has started. Your vet should be consulted regarding the correct dosage and timing of administration of these drugs, but they do have side effects. Dosage of

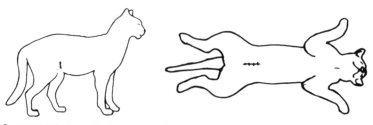

Spay wound after a 'flank' approach   Spay wound after a 'midline' approach

drugs should be under the control of your vet. Some cats do not tolerate them as well as others. Try to avoid extended periods of time on drugs.

- Artificial induction of ovulation (discussed later in this chapter).

The spay operation

The female cat is sterilised, or neutered, in an operation commonly called a 'spay'. Most veterinary surgeons remove not only both ovaries but also most of the uterus.

The operation is performed with the cat deeply asleep under the influence of a general anaesthetic. She feels nothing. After clipping the fur from the incision site, the nurse cleans and sterilises the skin. The surgeon, using sterile instruments, opens the abdomen either on one flank or in the mid-line near the belly button, according to the surgeon's particular technique.

The two ovaries and the uterus are removed, and any blood vessels and stumps remaining are carefully tied off ('ligated'). The opening in the muscles is usually closed with sutures (stitches) that will eventually 'dissolve' or be absorbed by the body. The skin is usually closed with non-absorbable sutures, which are removed, usually about 10 days after the operation.

Q *What precautions should I take after the spay operation?*

The cat is usually hospitalised for 8–24 hours during which time she is spayed. When she is allowed home you should keep her confined indoors until you are certain she is mentally alert and physically capable of walking freely. This usually takes 24 hours. Cats recover from surgery quickly and are soon back to normal.

After an anaesthetic, offer the cat a small drink. If she accepts it and does not vomit, further small amounts can be offered. Do not give food for at least 12 hours after the anaesthetic. Don't overfuss. Give her a little reassurance and a lot of peace and quiet.

The most common complication to occur is if the cat removes her sutures or has them removed for her by another pet. If the wound gapes open, it might have to be resutured. Bandaging the wound is not practicable, and you cannot watch the cat for 24 hours a day. An Elizabethan collar might be necessary. Often the wound will not gape open, even if the sutures are removed. If this is the case, confine the patient to a cage or small room. This will minimise movement and therefore strain on the wound. If there is any doubt as to whether the wound should be resutured, revisit your vet for an assessment of the situation.

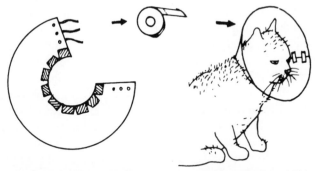

An Elizabethan collar can be fashioned from firm plastic or cardboard. This collar must fit snugly, or the cat will remove it. Once it is in place, leave it on — 24 hours a day — until it is no longer necessary

Q *After being spayed, will my cat still attract male cats?*

The neutered female no longer comes on heat and therefore this powerful, almost irresistible attraction to males is lost. The male still recognises her as female, so there is still a vague attraction for the tom, however, his attention is usually transient.

Q *Will she become fat and lazy?*

Not necessarily. Because she is no longer functioning as nature intended, there are not the constant demands and physiological drains of rearing kittens. As a result, the cat could put on weight. If you are careful, watch her diet and encourage exercise, obesity can usually be avoided.

Q *Will spaying alter her character? Wouldn't it be better to have a litter first or at least a period on heat?*

No. The cat returns to her pre-heat personality whether she goes off naturally or is spayed. Having litter is not believed to change her character permanently.

Q *Why not just 'tie her tubes' (tubal ligation)?*

Because the cat would continue to come into heat (the ovaries would still be active) with all the disadvantages of attracting toms, fighting and wandering. Certainly, she would not become pregnant, so there are certain advantages to the operation. Most people want to avoid all the associated nuisances of a queen on heat as well as just avoiding unwanted kittens.

NEUTERING THE MALE

While the female cat's personality is unaffected by being spayed, the male's is dramatically changed by castration. Male cats are dominated by their sex drive, and will wander, fight and mate whenever there is a queen on heat. Entire toms can be unpleasant in other ways. They mark out their territory with urine, which has a penetrating, offensive and persistent smell. Toms fight ferociously and are often responsible for serious wounds and abscesses in other cats. Entire males should not be allowed to roam free—they are a menace. The neutered male, on the other hand, can make an excellent pet. Castration, especially if performed before puberty, results in the loss of the sex drive and all its undesirable sequellae.

Castration is a simple surgical procedure. It is painless when performed under a short, general anaesthetic. Both testicles are removed. This removes both the cat's ability to produce sperm and the major source of the hormone testosterone, which is responsible for the fiery sexual drive of the tom.

There is occasionally some confusion with the vasectomy operation, which is used as a contraceptive method in humans. In a vasectomy, the testicles are not removed. Instead, the spermatic cord is tied so that sperm can longer be ejaculated during intercourse. Because the testicles are left intact, the production of testosterone is not halted, so the sex drive is not inhibited. Nor is there any change in the human's secondary sex characteristics, such as pubic hair patterns, muscle development and body hair.

In the tom cat, it is eminently desirable that the sex drive does cease, and with it the highly undesirable secondary sex characteristics of urine spraying, aggression and fighting.

A vasectomised cat does have some uses. A stud owner could use one to terminate heat in a queen if she is not ready to have a litter. After being mated by a vasectomised male, the queen will cease to call, but does not become pregnant. Vasectomised males could also play a big role in reducing the excessive cat population. If they were released into the wild, or into areas where the cat population was expanding too quickly, then sterile matings would reduce the number of kittens produced.

Q   *Is it fair to castrate toms?*

The argument for castration is overwhelming. There are tens of thousands of homeless cats in every major city. These cats prey on native birds and animals, and can wreak havoc with domestic pets. They are noisy and they smell. The entire tom is dominated by his sex drive—he will mate whenever possible. He leaves a pungent urine trail to mark his passage, plus sundry victims of fights, left with wounds and abscesses. Entire toms do not make suitable pets. The neutering operation is painless. The tom has no idea what has happened—he simply loses his sex drive. It is not a matter of 'missing out'. The neutered male has no desire to mate.

CRYPTORCHIDISM

There should be two testicles present in the scrotum. In some toms, one or both testicles fails to descend to their normal position in the scrotum (called retained testicles). If only one is absent, the cat is termed a monorchid. If both are absent, he is a cryptorchid.

The testicle must be positioned outside the body cavity if it is to produce viable sperm. Sperm are produced at temperatures below body temperature. A retained testicle can still produce hormones (so that the cat behaves like a male), but produces only sterile sperm.

Monorchid cats should not be used for breeding, as this condition could be hereditary.

Treatment
It is debatable whether treatment should be contemplated, other than to castrate the cat. Castration of these cats is not as straightforward as for normal males. An exploratory abdominal operation may have to be performed to find the missing testicle(s). If the abdominal testicle is not removed there is a high probability that it will become cancerous.

Various drugs and surgical techniques have been promoted as possible treatments for retained testicles. We do not support their use.

INHERITED DISEASES

For thousands of years cats bred according to the hard and uncompromising rules of natural selection. The fittest, strongest and best adapted animals survived. As a result, the cat is extremely well suited to its biological niche as a hunter of small rodents and mammals. The

wild cat is tough, cunning and resource-
ful. When humans began to take an
interest in cats, they initially encouraged them as a means of controlling
vermin. Gradually, the cat became
partly domesticated, and humans
started to select those they preferred
and bred only with them. The crite-
rion for selection was no longer the
bitterly fought battle for survival.
Instead, selection was based on more

The Scottish Fold

mundane characteristics, such as temperament, coat colour, body
conformation and even eye colour. Inevitably, the inherent resistance
of the domestic cat declined. We have certainly achieved a more
manageable cat, but breeders should be aware of the enormous
potential for selecting for the wrong reasons. Fortunately, selective
breeding has not yet made disastrous inroads to the basic health and
viability of the cat as has already occurred with some breeds of dog,
such as the bulldog, the Pekinese and the Chihuahua.

Inherited defects are usually responsible for pain or discomfort
that can generally only be controlled, not cured. Some inherited
defects are quite well known, for example, deafness of blue-eyed,
white cats, cleft palates, hare lips and umbilical hernias.

The 'Scottish fold' cat is a concern. If the gene that produces the
folded ear is present in only one parent, then (on average) half of
their kittens will have not only folded ears but skeletal abnormalities of the tail and lower limbs as well. If the gene is present in both
parents, then (on average) half the potential kittens will be lost
because of a lethal genetic effect. Surely this is too high a price to
pay for a breeder's whim.

In the Siamese breed there was a trend to accept inherited
defects, and even to include mention of them in the breed stan-
dards. So squint eyes and a kink in the tail were deemed to be
'acceptable'. Reason has prevailed, and these characteristics are
being bred out again—fortunately for Siamese cats.

The Manx (tail-less) gene has an influence over the entire vertebral column, not just the tail. If a kitten inherits the dominant Manx
gene from both parents, this is lethal. The kitten dies before birth. If
it inherits only one Manx gene, it will be tail-less, but many also
suffer from maldevelopment and partial fusion of the spine.

Breeding for fashionable whims, and not for efficient function, can
cause discomfort or even pain for the unfortunate cats involved. The
short-nosed, longhaired breeds have a tendency to suffer from breathing difficulties, crowded mouths (and therefore dental disease), over-

shot jaws, tear duct malformation, intolerance of heat, an increased tendency to dermatitis and a general deterioration in temperament that makes them more inclined to be shy or aggressive. We might admire their looks, but has it been worth it?

Genetics is a fascinating subject, but can be complex. It is not within the scope of this book to cover it adequately. If you want to know more, ask your vet to recommend or lend you a suitable book.

The shortnosed breeds suffer unnecessary discomfort due to fashionable breeding whims

BREEDING

Assuming you have carefully considered the situation and have decided to breed, there are many things you should know and do. First things first: Prepare the queen for pregnancy with vaccinations and worming.

Vaccinations

The queen passes important protective antibodies to her kittens. Some are transferred while the kittens are still in her uterus, but most are given with the first milk, or 'colostrum'. The immunity conferred by these antibodies is strong but temporary, and the antibody level in the kittens gradually falls to below protective levels a few weeks after birth. You can ensure that the kittens get the maximum protection by correctly vaccinating the queen. Recommended vaccination times are either before mating or during the last three weeks of pregnancy. It is not recommended that the queen be vaccinated during early pregnancy, as the kittens could be adversely affected.

You should vaccinate against feline infectious enteritis and preferably the feline respiratory diseases. Other vaccinations might be recommended by your vet, such as rabies or leptospirosis. Consult your vet for details.

Worming the queen

The queen should be wormed before mating to help ensure that she is in good physical condition for pregnancy. You could take a sample of her faeces to your vet for analysis to determine what parasites she is carrying, or simply use a product the vet recommends to control possible roundworm, hookworm and tapeworm infestations.

Treat the queen again for roundworm either a few days before the expected delivery or a day or so after. Use a mild, safe drug such as Piperazine.

Around queening, you should wash the queen's nipples to remove any worm eggs stuck to the skin. There can be huge numbers of these, and the kittens might otherwise ingest them while sucking.

Q   *At what age should a queen be bred?*

If nature equips the queen to breed from about six months of age onwards, then who are we to deny that this is the correct time to mate and breed? Nevertheless, experience suggests that the queen is better able to cope with the stress of pregnancy if you wait until she is more than 10 months and preferably 12 months old. She will be stronger and more physically mature and therefore better able to channel her resources into the developing kittens.

Q   *What about the male?*

Any age after puberty is theoretically all right. A calm, experienced queen will accept him without much fuss, but he might need either age or experience before he can successfully be used at stud with flighty, nervous females.

THE BREEDING CYCLE

The expressions *being on heat, on call* or *in season* are all euphemisms for that stage in the queen's sexual cycle when she is attractive to toms and ready to mate. Her ovaries are active and have produced a crop of eggs that are nearly ready to be released (ovulation) for possible fertilisation by sperm from the tom. The ovaries also produce hormones, which are responsible for the various behavioural and physical changes that occur in the queen at this time.

The age a queen comes into heat usually given as 7–9 months. This varies according to factors such as the queen's breed and nutritional state, the time of the year, the presence of other cats, housing and even sudden changes in the weather. Some cats come into heat as early as four months old. The longhaired breeds tend to achieve sexual maturity later than most—at 10 months or older.

Factors influencing when a queen comes into heat

The length of daylight, the weather and socialisation are factors that influence when a queen comes on heat. Length of daylight is probably the most important factor. Queens usually come into heat as the daylight hours lengthen in spring, then continue to cycle until the short winter days set in. While there are peaks of sexual activity in autumn and late spring, most cats cycle more or less continually throughout the longer daylight period—unless the cycle is interrupted by pregnancy, as it usually is.

Sudden changes in the weather can put queens off heat or, alternatively, bring non-cycling queens into heat.

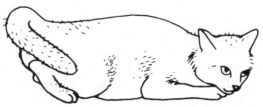

A queen in 'heat' will crouch, lift her pelvis and hold her tail to one side

Indoor cats that have little contact with other cats call less frequently, less vocally and for shorter periods than do outdoor cats in contact with others.

The signs of a queen on heat

The first sign is a slight swelling of the vulva, which also becomes slightly moist. This change is easily missed.

Changes in behaviour are more obvious. The queen crouches, lifting her pelvis and holding her tail to one side. She might tread with her hind feet. The queen's miaow becomes lower pitched and much more frequent—hence the expression *calling* or *on call*. She usually becomes restless and more affectionate, rubbing up against legs and rolling in front of you. To determine whether your cat is on heat, stroke her firmly down her back with the side of your forefinger. If she is on heat she will respond by crouching down and thrusting her pelvis up, will twitch her tail to one side and miaow intermittently. As the mating urge becomes stronger, the cries become intense. Inexperienced owners might believe their cat is in pain as she rolls about, kneads the carpet and howls.

The 'calling' phase usually lasts 5–10 days with intervals of 2–3 weeks between, but there is great individual variation. Once a particular queen has established a pattern, this pattern normally repeats itself each season. After the cat has been mated she will go off call within a few days. If she is not mated, calling can continue for around 10–14 days. Queens living in groups call more often and for longer than do solitary queens. If she has had more than one litter, a queen tends to stay on call for a long time if she is not mated. Cats return to call after only 2–3 weeks, and this cycle continues unless the queen becomes pregnant or until the shorter days and cooler weather return.

OVULATION

Unlike most animals, cats do not spontaneously release eggs from the ovary. It is the mating act that stimulates the final development of the eggs in the ovary and their subsequent release about 24–30 hours later. The eggs then go via the fallopian tubes (where fertilisation usually takes place) to the uterus. In most animals and in women, the eggs are released spontaneously as part of the sexual cycle. Timing of mating in cats is therefore of little consequence, in contrast to the situation in bitches where mistiming of mating is one of the most common causes of infertility.

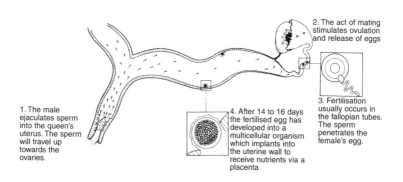

2. The act of mating stimulates ovulation and release of eggs

1. The male ejaculates sperm into the queen's uterus. The sperm will travel up towards the ovaries.

4. After 14 to 16 days the fertilised egg has developed into a multicellular organism which implants into the uterine wall to receive nutrients via a placenta

3. Fertilisation usually occurs in the fallopian tubes. The sperm penetrates the female's egg.

Usually four eggs are released for possible fertilisation, although it could only be one or two, and a dozen or more have been known to be simultaneously ovulated. Not all the eggs necessarily become fertilised, nor do all fertilised eggs develop to result ultimately in a kitten born 60-plus days later.

Artificial induction of ovulation

The artificial induction of ovulation is sometimes used as a method of taking the queen off

Artificially inducing ovulation

heat. A glass rod (such as a rectal thermometer) or a cotton bud ('Q' tip) is introduced into the vulva and gently twirled around. This action mimics the insertion of the male penis and usually stimulates ovulation. The queen will then go off call. A state of 'false pregnancy' then ensues, which can delay the return to heat by a month and sometimes longer. Some breeders have a vasectomised tom to perform the same function: a sterile mating that takes the queen off call until a more convenient time for mating with a fertile stud.

MATING

Mating is more likely to be successful if the queen is taken to the male, rather than vice versa. Once signs of heat are established, take the female to the stud fairly soon so that she becomes accustomed to the different environment. Long journeys should be avoided as they can stress the queen and put her off heat.

The receptive female will allow the male to approach

Place the queen in a pen adjacent to the male's run. After she has settled, allow her to come out and wander about in her own time. Keep the male confined. The queen will gradually become conditioned to her new environment. When she approaches his pen and begins to show interest, the stud's gate may be opened.

If the queen is receptive, she will allow the stud to approach her, then to sniff, touch and lick. This foreplay is important to many queens, and essential for a successful mating with them. The absence of this foreplay might be one reason why artificial insemination has not been as successful in cats as in some other species.

The queen will adopt the mating position when she is ready. She crouches down, with pelvis raised and tail held to one side. The male will straddle the queen, holding her between his forelegs and seizing the skin over the back of her neck.

The male's penis normally points backwards. On erection this changes. As the penis engorges with blood and swells to erection it curves under and between the male's thighs to be directed forwards. The male introduces his penis into the queen's vagina, simultaneously thrusting with his pelvis. Ejaculation of sperm usually occurs within 5–15 seconds. The male usually emits a deep growl during ejaculation.

(A) This insert shows the male's penis ejaculating sperm into the females's vagina; (B) The male straddles the female; (C) As the male withdraws the queen screams and may lash out at the retreating male

The queen screams stridently. As the male dismounts, she may turn and lash out at him. This is common and not cause for concern. It may be caused by pain on the withdrawal of the penis, as it has numerous barbs or spikes at the tip. (However, the same scream and paw slash sometimes occurs when a smooth glass rod is introduced then withdrawn instead of the penis.) The queen usually relaxes quite quickly after mating and commences a typical post-mating sequence of rolling and grooming herself.

The male's penis has numerous barbs or spikes at its tip

Your role

It is prudent to have an observer present during this sequence in case the pair do not accept each other. The queen might not be quite ready, or the male might become too aggressive. Some queens simply won't tolerate some males, yet will accept others with ready compliance. In these situations, an ugly confrontation could develop and one or both cats might be hurt unless they are separated.

Beware when approaching cats in a mating situation. You could be badly scratched or bitten, even by your own cat.

Cats usually mate several times over one to three days, and maybe even three or four times within an hour. Most stud owners like to ensure that at least two matings occur.

Too much human interference is likely to reduce the chances of a successful mating.

Some problems that might interfere with mating

Queen not ready
The most common cause of failure to mate is that the queen is not ready. The owner might have introduced her to the stud too early, or the stress of entering an unfamiliar environment might temporarily put her off heat. The queen must be given a chance to settle down and become comfortable with her new surroundings. If she refuses to mate, or gives no sign of being receptive, be prepared to wait. Try again in a day or two.

Male aggression
The stud might be too aggressive and reluctant to let the female near, or he might frighten her with his aggression. Tranquillisers could be useful, but the correct choice of drug is important. Many tranquillisers reduce male fertility. Seek veterinary advice.

Inexperience
A very young, inexperienced or exceptionally quiet male might lack the vigour to achieve a successful mating. Some sexual aggressiveness is necessarily, especially if the queen has a dominant character. These restrained stud toms should be mated with an experienced and compliant queen. This usually improves subsequent performance.

Abnormalities
Occasionally there could be a physical problem or defect preventing the male from copulating. A possibility is that hair becomes wrapped around the penis, or the presence of crystals in the bladder and penis could cause obstruction to sperm or pain on erection. A complete physical examination is warranted, with special attention paid to the penis and testicles.

ARTIFICIAL INSEMINATION

Artificial insemination is possible in cats. It has not been widely used. In this technique, semen is collected from the male then injected into the vagina of the queen.

One method sometimes used is to allow the male to mate with another queen, then to harvest the sperm by syringing it from her vagina and subsequently injecting it into the queen you wish to be fertilised. There are a few situations in which this procedure could be useful; for example, it could be used if it was impracticable to take the queen to the stud for reasons of distance or temperament. If you are interested in knowing more, you should consult your vet. Correct techniques and proper handling of the delicate sperm are essential to maximise your chances of success.

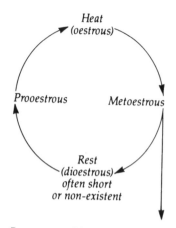

Pregnancy or false pregnancy can break the cycle here

ABORTION

Abortion (or spontaneous miscarriage) means the premature expulsion of dead kittens from the uterus. Abortion of kittens is more common in pure bred cats. Quite often the cat's owners are not aware of the abortion because the queen, being fastidiously clean, eats the aborted foetus and cleans the discharges so they are not observed.

DETERMINING PREGNANCY

The length of a cat's pregnancy (the gestation period) is usually between 63 and 70 days. The average is 65 to 66 days. Some cats give birth to normal, healthy kittens a little earlier or later than this range.

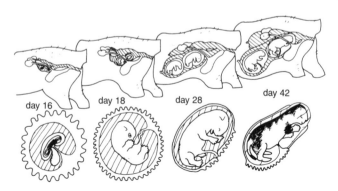

day 16   day 18   day 28   day 42

By 28 days the kittens can be felt in the abdomen as discrete, round lumps in the uterus. They are about the size of a child's glass marble. An experienced breeder or vet will palpate the uterus gently and not harm the kittens. If you decide to have a feel, be careful not to exert too much pressure or upset the queen. At 35 days a distinct rosy halo develops around the nipples. The breasts begin to develop, starting with the nipples, which enlarge and become more prominent. From 35 days onwards until term there is a detectable increase in the size of the abdomen. By 50 days the kittens can be seen or felt to move. By this stage the mass in the uterus is sausage-shaped, and the heads can be palpated.

If there is doubt as to whether the cat is pregnant and it is important to know, X-rays could be taken. You will have to wait until after the thirty-ninth day as the kittens' bones do not show up well until then.

False pregnancy

Following an unsuccessful or sterile mating, or following artificial induction of ovulation, the queen might show some of the early signs of pregnancy, such as enlargement of the nipples. Usually these misleading signs last only to the fortieth or forty-fifth day, then they terminate spontaneously. This situation is called false pregnancy or pseudopregnancy.

PREGNANCY

The queen does not require a lot of extra attention during pregnancy. Excessive feeding or overfussing can produce unnecessary problems. Do not increase the queen's ration until the last 2–3 weeks of pregnancy. The main drain on her reserves will occur when she is feeding the kittens, not during pregnancy itself.

Feeding

Overfeeding can produce problems. A fat queen with a 'lazy' uterus might be capable of only weak and perhaps ineffectual muscle contractions. Excessive fat around the pelvic canal and oversized kittens can add to the obese queen's difficulty in expelling the kittens at term, so that veterinary assistance might be required. If you are feeding a good, balanced diet there is no need for extra supplements of vitamins and minerals.

Do not be surprised or concerned if, in late pregnancy, the queen eats only a little at a time or seems to be only 'picking' at her food. Her abdomen is crowded with kittens. This makes it uncomfortable to fill up with large meals. By eating little but often she will usually consume her normal daily intake.

Some queens are eating about twice their normal ration by the end of pregnancy. This is all right so long as you do not start the increase too early. Be certain that the queen is not putting on fat. It is usually possible to offer food on an 'ad lib' basis from late pregnancy through to the weaning of the kittens. Most queens will not overeat. Have the food freely available, and the queen will help herself. Dry foods are especially suitable for this style of feeding.

Exercise

Within reason, normal exercise and activities should be allowed. Jumping from heights should be discouraged, especially in the last two weeks.

Drugs and insecticides

Beware of using powerful insecticides or harsh worming preparations during pregnancy. Check with your vet to see if the product you contemplate using is safe. If you take your cat to the vet for any reason, be certain to tell him/her that your cat is pregnant—or could be pregnant. Many drugs and vaccines are safe for the mother but could seriously harm the developing kittens especially if given in early pregnancy.

Kittening box

Ideally you should accustom the expectant queen to a suitable kittening area well before the due date. She will prefer somewhere quiet and dark. If you can, accustom her to a 'kittening box', which could be made from cardboard or wood. A wooden box has the advantage that shelves or ledges can be fitted to allow the kittens to shelter away from the queen when she rolls over. The kittening box can be lined with newspaper or towels, or anything clean and absorbent that can be disposed of or easily washed.

The queen might show a preference for kittening inside a

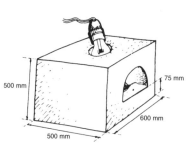

A home-made kittening box

wardrobe or cupboard, or under a bed. If feasible, put the kittening box in this preferred area (although obviously it will not fit under a bed). If she is showing a strong attraction to an area you definitely don't want her to kitten in—for example under the house or at the foot of your bed—you might have to block off that area.

The critical factors in determining the suitability of a place for kittening are that it is warm, dry and draught free. If the queen has a suitable bed, it will usually make a perfectly satisfactory 'labour ward' for her.

It is preferable for her to have the kittens at home where she is most likely to be relaxed in a familiar environment.

Signs that birth is imminent

A few days before the birth the queen usually becomes restless. She will pace the room, then fuss about, grooming herself frequently, paying special attention to her genitals and breasts. She might eat less, or even stop eating.

Sixty-five days is only the average term of pregnancy. There is a variation from 60 to 71 days which could still be normal for that particular queen.

About 12–24 hours before labour starts there is a transient drop in her temperature from the normal 38.5°C to around 37.5°C. We doubt that there is much to be achieved by continually sticking a thermometer in the poor cat's rectum just so that you are better informed and know when to prepare for the actual event. Some authorities recommend that you do. It's up to you.

Keep an eye on the queen to ensure she does not disappear into some dark and inaccessible place to give birth.

THE BIRTH

Most cats have their kittens without the need of the slightest help from you. Stand back, observe quietly from a distance and interfere only if necessary. Don't constantly hover over the queen. Your anxiety is infectious and only serves to upset the mother.

The strength and range of the maternal instincts are remarkable. Even experienced queens perform as if they have read a manual. However, nervous queens might not, and there is always the possibility of a hitch so be prepared just in case.

If the cat refuses to use the kittening box, it is better to let her have the kittens where she chooses (within reason) and move the lot to your prepared area only after the birth is complete—when all the kittens have been presented and are contentedly suckling.

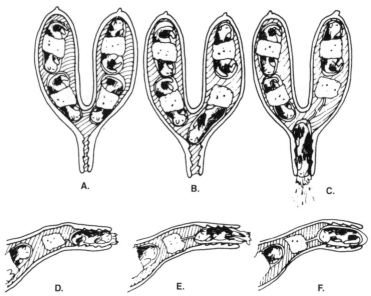

A. Prior to delivery. B. The cervix opens. The first kitten is forced into the pelvis; C. the membranes usually rupture as the kitten passes through the pelvic canal; D. E. both head first and feet first presentations are considered normal; F. sometimes the membranes fail to rupture. Note the placenta following, attached to the membranes

Labour in a cat is not the traumatic, long drawn-out process it can be in humans. Most queens deliver the kittens quickly and quietly. They will have them cleaned and feeding while you are still getting ready for the anticipated drama.

The first stage: preparation for delivery

Internally, the cervix dilates (opens wide). The ligaments of the pelvis have already relaxed to produce a relatively spacious passage for the kittens to pass through. The kittens are moved towards the pelvis by rhythmic muscular contractions of the uterus until the first in line is lying ready to be passed through the pelvis and out into the world.

The first stage lasts about 12 hours. It might take much longer. On the other hand, many queens start to produce within an hour of the apparent onset of labour. You might be able to observe the uterine contractions as the kittens are moved into position. The queen's breathing gradually becomes shorter and more rapid. Purring can be quite loud. Some tremble and become restless, looking around tentatively at their flank. Others might cry out. A nervous queen might become distressed and apparently confused.

In such a case, some quiet, calm reassurance is needed. Speak soothingly to her, stroke her and try to induce purring. In some cases—fortunately quite rare—tranquillisers are indicated. Use these only on veterinary advice.

The second stage: delivery

The queen usually lies over on one side or sits forward on her chest. The contractions of the uterus become strong and rapid, pushing the first kitten out through the pelvic canal, into the vagina and through the lips of the vulva. Contraction of the abdominal muscles and diaphragm help in these expulsive efforts. As the kitten is squeezed through the narrowest part of the birth canal (the pelvis), the membranes surrounding the kitten usually burst, releasing the thick, yellowish fluids which have bathed the kitten in the uterus and which now aid in lubricating the birth passage for its final few centimetres to life. In some cases, the fluid sac can be observed bulging through the lips of the vulva before bursting.

The kitten could be presented head first or feet first. Both presentations are considered normal. The queen rarely has trouble expelling a kitten. If more than 10 minutes pass after the first appearance of the nose or legs of the kitten without the delivery being completed, then the queen needs help (see the section 'Difficulties and how to deal with them' below).

Once the kitten has been delivered, the queen instinctively licks away the membranes surrounding the kitten. Her rough tongue serves to stimulate the kitten to breathe. Each kitten is thoroughly cleaned, and the umbilical cord is sheared off. (The umbilical cord joins the kitten to the membranes. It has been the kitten's lifeline for the past two months.) The umbilical cord is usually broken during the passage through the pelvis. If not, and if the queen fails to cut it or if it is bleeding, then you should tie it off.

The third stage: expelling the placenta

The third stage involves the expulsion of the placenta followed by a period of rest for the uterus before the next kitten is delivered.

The placenta is usually passed with the kitten or immediately after. The queen might eat the placenta. This does not appear to do her any harm. Some believe there are hormones or nutrients within the placenta that are helpful to the queen. Most breeders prefer the queen to eat only one placenta. Too many can produce indigestion or vomiting.

A common interval between kittens is 15–30 minutes. This varies, and can be much longer especially if the queen is overweight, old, or if there are many kittens and the uterus is becoming tired.

All the kittens are usually delivered within 2–4 hours. Occasionally it may take up to 24 hours.

YOUR ROLE

Don't interfere unless you have to. The birth and immediate aftercare provided by the mother is not only efficient and natural, it is also important to the formation of a bond between mother and kittens.

If the queen becomes preoccupied with one kitten, or a bit nervous or confused and fails to break the membranes around her kitten, you should do it for her. Don't rush in—give her a minute to adjust. If she takes too long you must clear the membranes from the kitten's face. After clearing the membranes, present the kitten back to the mother to be licked and cleaned. If she will not do this, you should rub the kitten dry with a rough towel. Be gentle, but thorough. This action dries the kitten, thus reducing the chance of chilling, and also stimulates the kitten to breathe.

As each kitten arrives, watch for the delivery of the placenta. Make sure that one placenta is passed for each kitten born. If a placenta is retained in the uterus it could lead to infection. If in doubt, have your vet check her about 12 hours after the last kitten has been delivered.

POSSIBLE PROBLEMS

Narrow pelvis

The kittens must pass through the pelvis. If this passage is too narrow, a Caesarean section may be required. Several conditions can lead to a narrowing or deformity of the pelvic canal. The two most likely are:

- Motor car accidents, in which the pelvis was fractured (this is surprisingly common).
- Rickets—a calcium imbalance or deficiency suffered when the queen was a kitten. This can result in spinal and/or pelvic deformity.

Bleeding cords

If the kitten is bleeding from the umbilical cord you must stop the blood flow quickly. This is not a common problem but could occur if, for example, the queen nips off the cords too short. Tie the cord off with dental floss or thread—preferably some that has been soaked in antiseptic first, but don't delay is this is not available.

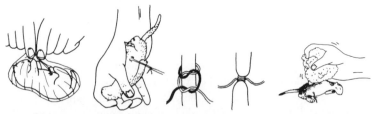

Break the membranes and clear them from the kitten's mouth and nose; if necessary, tie off a bleeding cord; cord tied off with a reef knot

Kitten not breathing

- Clear any membranes from the mouth.
- Rub the kitten vigorously with a piece of towelling. *Be gentle* —don't press down too hard and squash the kitten.
- If that does not succeed, hold the kitten between your hands and stretch your arms out in front of your body gently. Swing the kitten down towards the floor with the nose pointing down. Any mucus in the breathing passage should be expelled by this procedure. Repeat 2–3 times if necessary.
- If still no success, mouth to mouth resuscitation might be necessary.

When to call the vet

- Queen passes a green, yellow or bloody discharge *before* kittens are born. (This could indicate premature separation from the placenta or a uterus infection.)
- Queen is straining for ½ hour without success.
- Kitten's feet or nose presented but birth is not complete within 10–15 minutes. (Also read section on assisting birth.)
- Queen is anxious and upset, and the birth is not progressing.

If the kitten fails to breathe, rub it with a piece of rough towelling; to clear the breathing passages, it may be necessary to swing the kitten downwards, thus forcing the fluids out; mouth to mouth resuscitation may be necessary

- Too long an interval passes between delivery of kittens. More than three hours is abnormal. Sometimes a queen will have one or two kittens, appear perfectly normal, will suckle the kittens and be comfortable and content, but will then go back into labour next day to produce more healthy kittens. This particular situation does not require intervention on your part. A situation that *should* trigger your anxiety is when the queen is unsettled, uncomfortable and does not seem able to produce the next kitten. This is most likely to occur in overweight queens, or in queens that are debilitated or weakened for some reason.
- Oversized kittens. Occasionally an extremely large kitten is presented. This is especially likely if the queen is carrying only one or two kittens. The presenting history and signs are usually that the queen started labour normally, straining for a while, but since then has done nothing. Sometimes the kitten's legs will show, then disappear again. The treatment depends on many factors, but mainly on just how large the kitten is. A Caesarean section is usually performed. Some vets prefer an episiotomy under some circumstances (a minor surgical procedure in which the vulva opening is enlarged by means of cutting the tissue on either side).

EMERGENCIES

This section is designed to help you in an emergency. Obstetrics is not a field for amateur treatments. Whenever possible, get experienced or professional help. If this is not feasible, we hope the information below will help you make the right decision when a little assistance can ease a potentially awkward situation.

Abnormal presentation

The classic birth position is head first with the forepaws alongside the head. In about 40% of feline deliveries the hind feet come first, and this is also considered normal for the cat.

If the rump or tail comes first, with the hind legs tucked back under the kitten, this is termed a breech presentation. Kittens presented in this way are usually passed without much difficulty, but occasionally there is a physical or mechanical blockage.

Other presentations that might similarly obstruct the birth canal are: head back or head and neck back.

What to do (where professional help is not available)
- Wash your hands thoroughly.

- Lubricate your forefinger, preferably with surgical lubricant gel (available from veterinary suppliers or pharmacists), but white petroleum jelly will do.
- Gently introduce the finger into the queen's vulva. The angle of entry is not straight in, but slightly upwards. Take your time. Try to determine exactly what part of the kitten you can feel.
- If a leg is back, try to push the whole kitten slightly back into the uterus, then hook the offending leg forwards. You might require one finger to hold the kitten back, and one finger of the other hand to do the hooking.

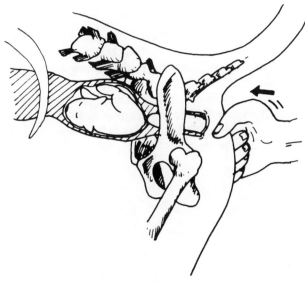

Before trying to reposition a kitten, first push it backwards. This takes pressure off the kitten and gives you room to manoeuvre the limbs

- Proceed similarly for a head back. Do not try to realign the kitten until after you have pushed it back a little. This gives you room to manipulate.
- If the kitten is normally placed (head and forefeet in pelvis or hind feet in pelvis) but the queen is having difficulty expelling it, lubrication of the birth canal might help.
- Push the lips of the vulva back to enlarge the opening for the emerging kitten. If the head is presented, you might be able to work the lips of the vulva over the kitten's head.
- Try to grasp as much of the kitten as possible, preferably with a piece of clean towelling. Never pull on one single limb—you risk seriously damaging it. Time your pulls to coincide with the

mother's uterine contractions. Exert the pressure of your pull on the kitten downwards as well as outwards from the vulva.

- By slightly rocking or rotating the kitten you may find it slips out more readily.

Retained placenta blocks the passage

Hook the placenta with a cleaned finger. If possible, grasp it with a piece of clean towelling or gauze. Exerting gentle pressure, slowly pull it out. *Don't* jerk as you may break it—or worse—cause bleeding.

No contractions

If the muscles of the uterus have become exhausted, whether from straining against an obstructed kitten or because the mother is in a poor or weakened condition, there is little you can do. Your vet might be able to induce contractions with an injection of oxytocin. If not, a Caesarean might be indicated. If there are no signs of contractions but you know, or suspect, that more kittens are still in the uterus, it is always a problem to know how long to wait. Table 4 provides a helpful guide.

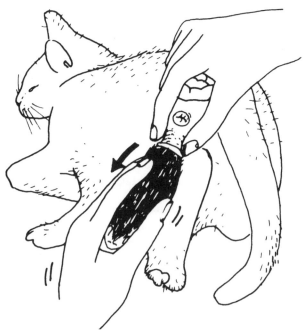

Pull gently outwards and downwards

Table 4: No contractions—interval before intervention

Queen bright, alert, comfortable previous kittens content, suckling.	Wait at least 2 hours. No real cause for concern.
Queen exhausted, lies on side occasionally. Panting. Neglecting kittens.	Wait no more than 2 hours. Less if queen's condition deteriorating.
Part of kitten presented—perhaps feet or tail, which subsequently either disappears back or there is no further progress.	Wait no more than 10 minutes, especially if queen is distressed and straining.
Fluids expelled, but no kitten presented.	Wait no more than 10 minutes.

THE CAESAREAN OPERATION

This operation is usually performed with the queen under a general anaesthetic, although it is theoretically possible to do it under local anaesthetic. Using sterile techniques to avoid infection or contamination, the surgeon opens the abdomen and brings the uterus up to the incision site. The uterus is then opened and the kittens removed. While an assistant attends to the kittens, the surgeon carefully stitches up the uterus and then the abdomen.

In most cases the queen is awake enough to suckle the kittens within 1–2 hours. If the operation is performed while the queen is still quite strong, the prognosis for a successful outcome is usually excellent. Unfortunately, many owners wait too long and fail to present the queen for examination until she is already exhausted. The kittens might already be dead, and the risks for the queen become much higher than they should be. Undue delay in opting for a Caesarean can put mother and kittens at risk.

AFTER THE BIRTH

It is worthwhile having a veterinary check of the mother and kittens. The queen will be examined to see that there are no kittens or membranes remaining, and you will be given whatever advice is necessary.

Some vets give postnatal injections of oxytocin, which is a hormone that causes the uterus to contract. This injection might help to clear any remaining debris from the uterus.

Feeding

The queen's food requirements increase dramatically once she starts feeding the kittens. Although at first she might not eat much at all, soon she could be consuming at least double her normal ration. By the time the kittens are 4–5 weeks old, she could be eating three times her normal ration.

It is difficult to overfeed a nursing queen. Feed a balanced diet. A good multivitamin/mineral supplement seems to help, in our experience at least. Allow free access to clean water. Beware of giving too much milk as this could precipitate diarrhoea, with potentially serious results.

Mastitis

Mastitis is infection or inflammation of one or more of the mammary glands (the breasts). Possible causes of mastitis include:
- Infection by bacteria.
- Physical knock or blow.
- Blocked teats, due to inverted nipples, damaged nipples or infection of skin involving the nipples.

Signs
- Queen refuses to feed kittens. Instead she gets up and moves away when they nuzzle in because of the pain.
- Affected gland(s) swollen, tense and painful, might be hot to the touch.
- Secretion from gland
  —watery (usually),
  —or blood-stained,
  —or thick, foul-smelling,
  —or normal in appearance but smells sour.
- Queen might be feverish.
- Sometimes the first sign is diarrhoea and/or colic in the kittens.

Treatment
The treatment depends on the cause. Seek veterinary advice. Antibiotics are usually indicated. Relief of pain may be achieved by bathing the affected gland with a flannel soaked in warm salt solution and by gently expressing a little milk, to relieve the build-up of pressure in the gland. The queen might resent treatment of the gland itself. Do not persist if she is becoming distressed by your efforts.

Vulval discharge

Some discharge from the vulva is normal for up to a week following the birth. Initially a copious, thick, brownish-red fluid is passed.

This gradually clears to a yellows or clear mucoid discharge. There should not be an offensive smell. Be concerned if:

- The discharge smells strongly.
- The discharge is persistent, bloody or a dark red or green in colour.
- The queen is lethargic, off her food, or otherwise unwell.

An abnormal discharge is usually due to an infection in the uterus, perhaps resulting from a retained foetal membrane.

Infected uterus

An infection of the uterus is serious. Infections can start with a retained placenta, a dead kitten or by an infection spreading from the vulva and vagina, for example, following contamination around the time of delivery. Wet and soiled bedding or similar unsanitary conditions are especially conducive to uterine infections (and mastitis).

Signs

- Fever (39.5°C plus).
- General malaise: lack of appetite, listlessness, dull coat.
- Discharge from vulva: instead of a normal post-natal discharge (which is light reddish and not foul-smelling), the discharge is thicker, smells strongly and might be greenish, yellow, or a deep red colour.

Treatment

Veterinary treatment is essential. You might have to wean the kittens if the queen's condition is poor, as she will be unable to feed them properly, and the stress of feeding them will further weaken her. It might be necessary to spay the queen.

Viral infections of queen and kittens

A potentially awkward situation can develop, especially in a cattery or breeding establishment if a queen is carrying a latent (subclinical) viral infection. This is termed the carrier state. The stress of birth and of lactation can allow multiplication of virus particles within the queen. She then sheds virus into her immediate environment. Susceptible cats can then become infected. The kittens might initially be temporarily protected by antibodies from the queen. This protection wanes with time. Once the level of protective antibodies falls below a critical level, the kittens themselves become infected.

This usually occurs when they are between 4 and 8 weeks of age. Kittens can be weaned and already have gone to new homes before they come down with a viral infection. They had actually contracted the infection from their mother, but the infection had been incubating for a few days. The stress of weaning or moving to a new home can be enough to allow the infection to flare up. Apparently healthy kittens can quickly become severely affected.

The most common virus involved is a herpes virus—causing feline viral rhinotracheitis (see feline respiratory disease in chapter 9, 'Infectious Diseases'). An extensive survey in the UK showed one in every three show cats to be a carrier. If you are in a situation where a carrier cat is present, eradication is difficult. Ideally, you should stop breeding, clear the premises of all cats for a year or two, then repopulate with fully vaccinated cats from a stud known to be clear of the problem. Understandably such a program is rarely feasible.

Research has shown that up to 80% of cats in an infected cattery are carriers of FVR. It is not usually feasible to cull them all. In any case it is difficult to identify the carriers or be certain that apparently healthy cats are not harbouring hidden (subclinical) infections.

Eclampsia

Eclampsia ('milk fever') is not supposed to be a common problem in cats. It could be more common than is recorded, especially in pure-bred cats fed a predominantly meat diet.

Cause
A certain amount of calcium must be present in the cat's bloodstream for normal function of muscle and other tissue. The calcium level can fall because of the abnormally high demands for calcium in production of the queen's milk and—to a lesser extent—before the kittens' birth in the formation of bone and other foetal tissues. If the blood calcium levels fall below a critical level, eclampsia results.

Signs
- Nervousness, anxiety.
- Rapid, shallow breathing.
- Muscle spasms.
- Apparent incoordination, possibly developing into collapse or convulsions.

Treatment
Calcium is required. In critical situations it must be given intravenously. Intravenous treatment can be dangerous. Your veterinary

surgeon will carefully monitor the cat while giving the calcium. It might be necessary to wean the kittens as continuing drains of calcium are likely to result in recurring attacks. If this condition occurs in a queen the diet should be rectified so that it does not happen again.

UTERINE PROBLEMS

The female reproductive system in cats remains healthier if pregnancy takes place on a regular basis. Pathological changes to the uterus that can lead to infertility and infection are more likely to occur in the older queen who has not been spayed. Bacterial infection can lead to pyometra (i.e. a pus-filled uterus).

Signs
The signs of pyometra are:
- A foul-smelling vulval discharge in some cases.
- Lethargy, loss of energy.
- Weight loss.
- Loss of appetite.
- Increased thirst.
- Increased urination.
- Uterine enlargement, which can sometimes be detected by the veterinarian on abdominal palpation.

In some cases cats are surprisingly well, and uterine enlargement might be the only indication of the presence of the disease.

Treatment
The best and most effective treatment is to put the cat on a course of antibiotics and to spay her, as the probability of successful breeding following treatment is very low.

8 CARE OF THE NEWBORN KITTEN

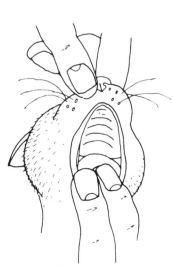

Normal palate

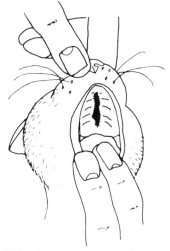

Cleft palate—they are sometimes less severe than this. In others, virtually the entire roof of the mouth is absent

Usually you can leave the care of the kittens entirely to the queen. For the first few days after the birth the queen will spend almost all her time with them. If the kittens suck vigorously and sleep soundly, there is no cause for concern.

Excessive handling of the kittens can create unnecessary problems. You might, for example, make the queen anxious and unsettled. Very young kittens are quite delicate and can be hurt, especially by children who could inadvertently be excessively rough with them. Kittens are easily chilled, so too much time spent away from the protection of the queen's body warmth can be very stressful to the kitten.

Signs of problems

The first indication of trouble is often constant crying by the kittens. This means they are hungry, cold or both. If an individual kitten is rejected by the mother you should examine it carefully for any obvious defects, such as cleft palate, a severe hernia or lack of eyelids. Or the kitten might be poorly developed and undersized in comparison to its littermates. If the kitten is malformed or grossly abnormal it is probably better to destroy it quickly and humanely. The mother will usually abandon a weak kitten. This seems cruel to us, but it is a strong and natural instinct. Perhaps this natural culling of the weak is harsh, but it is also sensible.

If the queen rejects a kitten, but on examination it seems healthy, and especially if the mother is inexperienced or upset, then remove the kitten temporarily. Keep it warm, dry and draught free. After the mother has settled down, try to return the kitten to her. If she still refuses to accept it, you should milk a little colostrum (the first milk) from the queen and give it to the kitten. The colostrum contains antibodies, which are vital because they give the kitten a degree of protection against many diseases for the first few weeks of life. These antibodies can only be absorbed into the kitten's system during the first day of life.

If the kitten's are unsettled and crying, or have diarrhoea, or seem to be weak and unresponsive, try to discover the cause and correct it if possible. If necessary, consult your vet for advice. (See also 'Fading kittens' later in this chapter).

The kitten's eyes should be closed for the first week of life. If the eyes are open, examine them carefully. If the kitten lacks normal eyelids, it should be humanely destroyed. If lids are present, the future outlook is better, but you must keep the eyes lubricated or they could become dried and ulcerated. Artificial tears and other eye ointments are available from your vet.

If the kittens lack hair, but the skin is reddish, it could be that the hair has been licked off by the mother. If so, it will grow back by the time they are weaned. If the kitten is born without hair, other than a fine down on the muzzle (the skin in these cases is *not* red), the kitten could have an inherited alopecia (lack of hair), which is sometimes caused by a recessive gene. This condition does not improve with age. There is no treatment. Affected kittens should be euthanised and the mating program carefully examined to eliminate this fault in future litters.

On some occasions, fortunately rare, the queen kills and perhaps even eats

umbilical hernia

the kittens as they are born. This could be a form of hysteria, or it is sometimes associated with ripped umbilical cords. In this latter case, the mother makes the haemorrhage worse by licking or chewing at the bleeding stump. Eventually the kitten dies from the shock and blood loss.

If the queen tries to kill the kittens, you must remove them immediately they are born. Attempt to return them when the queen has calmed. If she is still aggressive, or refuses to mother them, it might be necessary to foster the kittens.

ABANDONED OR ORPHAN KITTENS

In many cases it is possible to find a foster mother for abandoned or orphaned kittens. In a large cattery this is particularly easy as most queens are cycling simultaneously, and therefore several litters can be born at the same time. Nursing queens usually readily accept new kittens. Try to mix the orphans in with a litter of the same age, otherwise small kittens will be bundled out of the way by bigger kittens and not able to compete for a fair share of the milk.

If a foster mother is not available, you might decide to rear the kitten yourself. Be warned: it will require a lot of your time, patience and effort. Sometimes the kittens die despite the best endeavours. On the other hand, success can be extraordinarily rewarding.

Nursing queens will usually readily accept another kitten

Hand-rearing orphan kittens

Orphan kittens must be kept in a warm, draught-free environment. They have no ability either to lose or gain heat, so you must control their body temperature for them. Normally, this precise temperature control is achieved by snuggling against the mother and among the other kittens. For the first week of their lives, the temperature should be kept about 30–33°C. You can then gradually lower the temperature every few days so that by the time the kittens are a month old, the temperature in their box is down to 31–25°C.

Heating can be provided by an overhead light or heating coil, but it is better to use a heating pad. Do not cover the entire floor of their box with the pad. Allow them about half the area for cooling off if they become overheated.

The bedding material will become soiled and wet and should be changed frequently. Something that is washable or disposable should be used. We prefer towelling, but you could use newspaper, old sheets, even a lambskin if you like.

Give the kittens a source of warmth that will substitute for the mother and that they can snuggle against, for example, a well-wrapped hot water bottle. It should be replaced every three hours during the night.

Feeding the orphan kitten

The first 24 hours

Feed as much of the queen's 'first milk' or colostrum as possible. It could be milked from the queen's nipples then fed to the kittens with an eye-dropper. As colostrum contains antibodies that are vital to the kittens' defences in their first weeks of life, every effort should be made to ensure that the kittens get at least some colostrum. The colostrum can be supplemented by making up a solution of glucose in water: Dissolve 4 teaspoons of glucose in a cup of boiled water. Feed 1–2 ml to the orphaned kittens every 3–4 hours. An eye-dropper or nursing bottle is usually adequate.

Cow's milk does not adequately replace queen's milk, as it is deficient in both protein and energy content. A

Do not overfeed

suitable replacement formula will be available from your vet in the form of a commercially produced artificial substitute.

How often to feed

Days 2–5: five times daily.
Days 6–14: four times daily.
Days 14–21: three times daily.

Feed the kitten only until it is comfortably full—not until the stomach is tight and distended. A kitten that is doing well will put on about 10 g weight per day in the first week, then gradually increase this rate of gain to about 20 g a day by the third week. Do not be surprised or concerned if there is a small loss in weight the first day. Progressive weight and feeding quantities should be recorded.

The replacement formula should be warmed to body temperature—about 38°C. Most kittens will suck from a doll's bottle or specifically designed nursing bottle. These are available from most vets or pet shops.

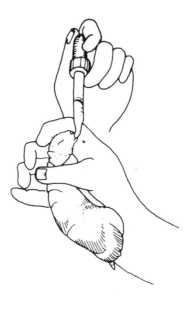

When feeding a very young kitten, first wrap it in towelling, with the paws restrained. Hold it firmly and gently. Put the rubber teat into the mouth. If the kitten does not automatically suck at the bottle, you might have to show it how. Using thumb and forefingers, gently move the kitten's lips up and down over the teat, mimicking or simulating the action of sucking lips. The kittens usually catch on quickly.

If the kitten will not suck, a stomach tube can be used. This is not difficult if you are careful. You must ensure the tube is passed down the correct length, and must make certain it is down into the stomach and *not* into the lungs before pouring in the formula.

After feeding the kitten, clean the area under the kitten's tail with a piece of rough towelling that has been dampened with warm water. This mimics and substitutes for the mother's tongue and stimulates the kitten to urinate and defaecate—both very necessary functions, albeit unpleasant for you.

The consistency of the kitten's stools will give you a guide to whether you are feeding the right strength of replacement formula. Normal stools are putty-like in consistency and a yellow colour. If diarrhoea develops you should dilute the formula. If the diarrhoea is persistent or severe, immediately consult your vet. Diarrhoea in the young kitten can be serious and should be controlled as quickly as possible.

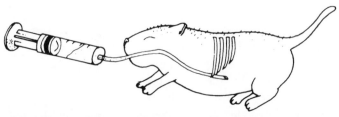

Measure the distance from the kitten's nose to its last rib. Mark this distance on the stomach tube and pass it down to that distance AND NO FURTHER

WEANING THE KITTENS

Most kittens can be weaned from the queen or the replacement formula on to solids by 3–4 weeks of age. The weaning procedure is not difficult. The method is to offer foods of gradually increasing consistency and complexity. At first, the kittens will puddle in among the food, feet and all, but they soon learn to lap and then to eat. Initially, offer the kittens normal replacement formula in a shallow dish instead of in a bottle. Let them suck your finger, then gradually lower the finger into the dish of milk. Start to add a little mashed egg, homogenised cooked meat or baby food. Other foods that can be gradually introduced include cottage cheese, yoghurt and commercial kitten foods.

It is essential to wean the kitten on to a variety of foods, otherwise the kitten could become hooked on a certain type of food for life. Just like babies, kittens should experience a range of tastes and textures early in life.

FADING OR SICK KITTENS

A 'fading kitten' is one that is not gaining weight properly and might be constantly crying out or abnormally passive and unresponsive. In approximate order of incidence, the possible causes include: inadequate milk supply, cold stress, infection of the navel, viral infections, mastitis or metritis and toxic milk, which are discussed below.

Inadequate milk supply

Kittens weigh, on average, between 90 g and 140 g at birth. If the queen's milk supply is adequate they should gain about 10 g per day, although they sometimes lose weight for the first day or two, and this is within normal expectations. The only way to be certain whether the kittens are developing satisfactorily is to weigh them daily. If there is any doubt, start a diary and chart their progress.

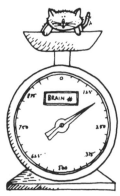

Weigh the kitten daily

The queen's milk supply is often scanty immediately after the birth, but should improve rapidly. You can determine whether the supply is good by gently squeezing a nipple between thumb and forefinger. You should readily be able to express a few drops of milk. An inadequate milk supply might only be temporary. By improving the queen's nutrition and perhaps by resolving any possible stresses on her, the milk production will often improve dramatically.

If the queen is not able to produce enough milk it might be necessary to supplement their food, or to foster one or more of the kittens, or even to raise the kittens as orphans.

Cold stress

Kittens are extremely sensitive to cold. They are unable to warm themselves if they become chilled. Undetected draughts, inadequate housing or damp bedding can lead to cold stress and loss of kittens. Cold kittens feel cold. They are sluggish and usually cry only weakly, then stop crying. They attempt to suckle but desist after a short time.

Diagnose cold stress by taking their temperature. Make sure you shake the thermometer right down first. A temperature lower than 37.5°C is worrying. Lower than 37°C is critical. Cold kittens should be slowly, gently rewarmed. Rapid heating can lead to shock or even to burns.

Infection of the navel

A bluish tinge around the stump of the umbilical cord (navel or belly button) is a sign of an infection of the navel. If left untreated, it could develop a pus discharge. Newborn kittens have little resistance, and a cord infection could flare into a serious condition quickly. These cord infections are especially likely if the bedding is soiled or wet.

Paint the stump with an antiseptic. If the kitten is not suckling you might have to give it supplementary food. Seek veterinary assistance early if the discoloured area is enlarging or if pus develops. The kitten will probably need antibiotics.

Navel infection ('navel ill')

Viral infections

The queen could be a carrier of various viral infections. The stress of late pregnancy is usually enough to allow the virus within the queen to multiply, resulting in a period of virus shedding at the time of, or just after, the birth of the kittens.

The most commonly involved viruses are those of the feline respiratory disease complex. The kittens usually have some immunity to these viruses, but it could be overcome, resulting in respiratory problems or even an overwhelming infection that will probably kill the kitten. Other viruses that could be similarly involved include feline panleukopeaenia (FIE) and feline leukaemia virus (FeLv). For more detail, refer to chapter 9, 'Infectious Diseases'.

One of the herpes viruses could be an important factor. The newborn kitten's temperature is below that of the mother, and this slightly lower temperature is ideal for this virus to thrive. So a herpes virus infection contracted from the mother could flare in a kitten, even though it has caused no apparent problem in the mother, resulting in a range of possible conditions from diarrhoea to pneumonia or even septicaemia.

Mastitis or metritis in the queen

Bacterial infections of the queen are most likely to involve either the mammary glands (mastitis) or the uterus (metritis). The kittens could also become infected, resulting in a range of possible conditions from diarrhoea to peneumonia or even septicaemia.

Sour milk

Sour milk is also called toxic milk. If the mother has mastitis or metritis, toxins could build up in the milk and cause sour milk. Kittens with this condition will cry and be bloated, with rough coats and raw, inflamed anuses. The kittens should be hand-reared until the mother's milk returns to normal. If the queen takes some days to recover, she might not return to full milk production, so the kittens might need some supplementary food.

Kittens usually refuse to suck from a queen with sour milk

SEXING YOUR KITTENS

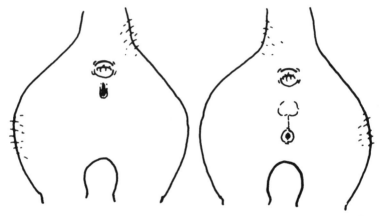

Female: The genital opening is slit shaped and quite close to the anus

Male: The genital opening is round. If you gently press under the opening a penis may be extruded. The distance between the anus and the genital opening is relatively greater than in a female

9 INFECTIOUS DISEASES

FELINE INFECTIOUS ENTERITIS

INFECTIOUS
DISEASES

FATAL

Feline infectious enteritis (FIE), also called panleukopaenia and incorrectly called cat distemper, is a major cat disease. It is caused by a very resistant and easily transmitted virus, and was for many years the scourge of the cat population. Fortunately, an effective vaccine is available, and outbreaks are now relatively uncommon. FIE is not contagious to people, dogs or other animals except for cats.

The virus incubates in the cat's body for 2–10 days before signs start. The affected cat sheds the virus in large numbers even before clinical signs develop, and this continues for about a week. After that, the cat might shed the virus intermittently even after recovery, maybe for months. Therefore only a fully vaccinated cat should be introduced into the household for the next 12 months.

Not all cats that contract the virus causing FIE are affected in the same way. There are four syndromes associated with FIE, although not all cases fit neatly into one category or the other.

Syndrome 1: sudden death

In this, the most severe form, the virus multiplies and spread so rapidly that the victim becomes ill and dies in less than a day—often before any warning signs appear. The owner might mistakenly think that the cat has been poisoned. Kittens younger than 6 months are more likely to be the victims of this syndrome than adult cats.

Syndrome 2: severe illness

In this syndrome, the course of feline infectious enteritis runs 3–7 days and might be fatal. The main sign is profuse, severe diarrhoea. Vomiting is also common. Affected cats are profoundly physically depressed. They usually refuse to eat but develop an apparent desire for water, often hovering over a water bowl but seldom drinking. Abdominal pain can be severe, causing the cat to adopt a hunched stance.

The cat becomes dehydrated, the coat assumes a rough feel and the skin becomes inelastic. You can test for this: pull up a generous pinch of skin over the back or neck. When released, this skin should immediately slide back into place. In the dehydrated cat it only slowly ebbs back into place.

Syndrome 3: few or no signs

Many cats exposed to the virus develop few or no apparent signs. After the virus has invaded the body, the cat's natural defences can be sufficient to prevent it from multiplying. This is termed a sub-clinical form, and it is a common form, especially in adult cats.

A cat with feline enteritis might hover over its water bowl

Syndrome 4: wobbly kittens

If a kitten is infected just before or after birth, damage can occur in the part of the brain responsible for balance (the cerebellum). Affected kittens lack coordination and balance, which causes them to stagger and tumble. Some kittens also develop chronic diarrhoea, probably due to severe damage to the developing gut lining. Incoordination might not be noticed until the kittens are several weeks old as before that all kittens are a bit wobbly. There is no treatment for kittens with this brain damage. This incoordination is permanent, and euthanasia is recommended if the kitten is unable to cope with basic activities such as eating or turning around.

Q *How does the infection spread?*

Affected cats shed vast numbers of the feline enteritis virus in all body secretions—urine, saliva, droppings and vomit. The virus is very tough and can persist in the environment for up to 12 months.

Treatment

Treatment of any viral disease is limited because an effective anti-viral drug is not available. Antibiotics kill or control bacteria, but they have no effect against a virus. Prevention, and not treatment, is the best way to control viral infections.

NURSING

Treatment should be under supervision of your vet. He/she might give fluids intravenously or under the skin to counter dehydration. Antibiotics are often given to prevent the invasion of bacteria. Drugs to reduce vomiting, diarrhoea and pain might also be indicated. We have found vitamins (especially the B group) very helpful.

Good nursing cannot be undervalued. Owners who are willing to apply time and effort to give fluids, medicine and tender loving care can make an enormous difference to the outcome. Feline enteritis is a serious disease, and the outlook is always guarded. Some cats have a strong will to fight the disease, others just seem to give up. The personality of your cat is a significant factor in determining the final outcome.

Prevention

Vaccination against FIE is strongly recommended. Vaccination does not give instant immunity. It takes 10–14 days after the first

VACCINATION

vaccination for a protective level of immunity to develop. The response to booster vaccination is much quicker, taking only a few days. Cats of any age can be vaccinated. Booster vaccinations are usually given annually.

Kittens can be given a temporary vaccination from 6 weeks of age and 'permanent' vaccination at 12–14 weeks. Usually annual revaccination is recommended, but ask your vet. In high-risk situations, such as following an outbreak, vaccination can be repeated as often as fortnightly from 2 weeks of age to 16 weeks.

It is not recommended that 'live' vaccines be used in pregnant cats. It is better to vaccinate queens before mating or to use a 'killed' vaccine in the last three

BOOSTER

weeks of pregnancy. By vaccinating the queen, a strong temporary immunity is passed to the kittens—99% of this immunity is passed in the first milk (the colostrum), so it is important that kittens suckle soon after birth to gain this protection.

FELINE RESPIRATORY DISEASE

INFECTIOUS

DISEASES

Feline respiratory disease (FRD) is also called cat flu or snuffles. It is a common viral infection of cats that resembles the head cold of humans. It is often incorrectly called cat flu (short for the influenza virus). It is not caused by the influenza virus. More than 80% of cases are caused by one of two agents: feline viral rhinotracheitis (FVR) or feline calicivirus (FCV). A vaccine that gives good protection against these viruses is available. Correct vaccination can save your cat from unnecessary discomfort.

Signs

Signs appear within 10 days of infection, usually within only 2–6 days. The effects of these viral infections vary from case to case and range from mild to extremely severe and potentially fatal. The course varies from one to three weeks. Siamese and Burmese seem particularly prone to the severe form.

Feline viral rhinotracheitis (FVR) infections are generally more severe than feline calicivirus infection (FCV), although mixed infections occur. The first sign is usually sneezing, then a watery eye discharge, which gradually becomes thicker and yellow. Crusts form around the eye. In severe cases, the eyes become swollen and puffy and can become ulcerated. It is important that these cases are treated by your vet as permanent damage can occur. There is frequent sneezing. The discharge from the nose changes from watery to thick and purulent. Because the cat's sense of smell is affected, the cat will often stop eating because food odours are necessary to stimulate the cat's appetite. Other signs include coughing, drooling saliva and mouth ulcers.

Improvement usually starts 5–7 days after the onset of signs, but severely affected cats might continue to deteriorate.

The pain in the cat's mouth and throat, gummed up eyes and nose, plus the loss of sense of smell and taste, can seriously reduce the cat's willpower. Some appear to give up the will to live. Good nursing is particularly important in these cases (see 'Treatment' below).

After recovery some cats can be left with residual damage to the sinuses, especially in the long-nosed breeds like the Siamese and orientals. This is most common if the cat is younger than six months old when infected. These cats might have recurring bouts of sneezing and persistent nasal discharge.

Feline calicivirus infection (FCV)

There are different strains of calicivirus, and the severity of the attack varies according to the strain. A frequent sign of calicivirus is ulceration of the tongue. Some calicivirus attacks produce virtually no signs. Others are almost as severe as FVR. In general the course is more moderate and lasts only 7–10 days. Ulcers may also

Ulcers on tongue of a cat with feline respiratory disease

appear on the paws, so the disease has been called 'paw and mouth disease'. (There is no connection with the more serious foot and mouth disease of farm animals.)

Other effects

Pregnant queens might abort (or 'miscarry') one or two weeks after exposure to the virus. Live virus vaccination of pregnant queens is not recommended.

The virus attacks the upper respiratory system (nose and throat), but it can predispose the cat to infections of the lower areas, especially in young cats. Bronchitis (infection of the bronchi) and pneumonia (infection of the lungs) are serious conditions. The cat should be put under veterinary care if there is any suspicion of chest involvement.

If kittens are affected before weaning there is a high risk of eye damage. If the eyes have not yet opened (that is, kittens younger than two weeks old) they should be taken to the vet to be checked.

Treatment

As with FIE, the best approach is not treatment but prevention by vaccination. Once cats have contracted the disease vaccination is too late.

Treatment is aimed at reducing the severity of the disease's effects and maintaining the cat in the best condition possible until natural immunity to the virus develops. Antibiotics are often used to control the serious and potentially fatal secondary bacterial infection. Eye ointments or drops may be prescribed. During treatment the eye should be kept free of discharge, and any crusts that form can be gently soaked and removed with damp cotton wool.

Fluids can be given by mouth if the cat will accept them. Broths are excellent and may stimulate the cat to drink. Glucose (not sugar) and water gives an easily assimilated energy source, or your vet may supply an electrolyte (body salt) replacement solution. If the cat is severely dehydrated the vet may inject fluids intravenously or subcutaneously.

Nursing

As with FIE the capacity for good nursing to improve the outlook is enormous. The patient should be kept in a warm, draught-free well-ventilated area. Gently clean away the eye and nose discharge using damp cotton wool balls. A thin smear of petroleum jelly below the eyes prevents the discharge sticking to the hair.

NURSING

Try to keep the cat eating. Highly flavoured foods are not as stimulating as strong smelling foods. Try fish or cheese, and warm the food a little to increase the aroma. Force feeding is successful in some cats, but do not persist if it causes distress and resentment.

Groom the cat. This increases its sense of well-being.

Vitamins help—especially the B group and vitamin C. Getting the cat to take them can be difficult, although highly palatable tablets and gels are available. Your vet could give vitamin injections.

Most of the treatment may have to be done by you, as many veterinary hospitals are reluctant to hospitalise these cats due to the highly infectious nature of the disease.

If you can induce your cat to purr it can ease breathing dramatically. Several purring sessions daily—a few minutes at a time is enough—can relieve distressed breathing and can greatly improve the cat's comfort.

Inhalation therapy

The aim of inhalation therapy is to loosen thick mucus from the nasal passages. Some cats cooperate well and seem to enjoy it, but if the cat appears distressed, do not persist.

One simple treatment is to put the cat in a cage and take it to the bathroom with you while you have a shower or bath. A more elaborate method is to use a bowl of hot water with an inhalation preparation such as eucalyptus oil or Friar's Balsam added. (Not too much! The cat has sensitive air passages and too much is irritating.) The cat is unlikely to sit over a steaming bowl, so put it in an open mesh basket or cage and suspend the cat over the bowl. A blanket thrown over the basket will prevent the vapour from dissipating.

Prevention

A vaccine injection against FVR and FCV can be given from 8–10 weeks of age. A second injection is needed 3–4 weeks later, and a third one 3–4 weeks after that. An annual booster is recommended. After the vaccination you might see mild signs of feline respiratory disease, but they are usually transient and not cause for alarm.

VACCINATION

Q *Is the vaccine effective?*

The protection derived from this vaccination might not be complete, especially if the cat is challenged by a high dose of virus as could occur during an outbreak or during a visit to a cattery. Vaccination

BOOSTER

decreases the severity of the disease, and a vaccinated cat is unlikely to suffer a fatal outcome.

Q *Is the virus very persistent? How long before infected premises are safe again?*

In contrast to the FIE virus, the respiratory disease viruses are frag- ile and can be destroyed by most common disinfectants and bleaches. FVR virus only survives about a day away from the cat. FCV might survive up to a week.

Q *Where is a cat likely to pick up feline respiratory disease?*

The spread of FRD is mainly from direct or indirect contact with infected cats. Cat shows, catteries and breeding esta- blishments are areas of potentially high risk, as many cats are brought toge- ther, often under stress. Stress can trigger off virus shedding in carrier cats. Infection comes from sneezing infected droplets and direct nose to nose contact in neighbouring cats.

Q *What is a carrier cat?*

More than 80% of cats that have recovered from FVR infection will intermittently shed the virus for up to a year and in some cases for a lifetime. So a cat might appear healthy but, especially when stressed, can shed virus and therefore infect susceptible cats in its immediate vicinity. Cats that have recovered from FCV infection are not quite so dangerous. About half shed virus for at least a month. Others can shed it for two or more years after apparent recovery.

Most carrier cats show no symptoms of the disease. Others show chronic signs such as runny nose or eyes.

Q *My cat has recovered from FVR. For how long is it immune against reinfection?*

Only 3–4 months.

Q *Can the cat catch flu from people?*

No. The virus cannot develop in a cat. But when we have a heavy cold we also shed large numbers of bacteria when we cough or sneeze, and the cat could develop a respiratory infection from these bacteria.

FELINE INFECTIOUS PERITONITIS

Feline infectious peritonitis, or FIP, is at present an uncommon viral disease in cats, but it is increasing in incidence. Only about 20% of cats exposed to the FIP virus develop signs of the disease. However, once signs do develop the course is almost invariably fatal, irrespective of treatment. Fortunately, many cats have a natural resistance to infection by the FIP virus, while others develop an immunity after exposure and infection without developing any clinical signs of disease.

In the terminal stages of FIP, the cat may develop a bloated, fluid-filled abdomen

There is no vaccine against FIP.

There are two forms of the disease: the 'wet' form, from which the disease gets its name, and the less spectacular but equally fatal 'dry' form.

The virus can be present in the cat's system for several weeks or months before signs appear. Young or debilitated cats, or cats suffering from some injury to their immune system, are most likely to be affected.

The wet form of FIP

The peritoneum is the membrane that lines the abdominal cavity and covers the abdominal organs. The peritoneum becomes inflamed and produces an exudate that slowly builds up in the abdomen, giving the cat a swollen, bloated appearance. Meanwhile, the cat loses appetite, becomes lethargic and is intermittently feverish. Sometimes the cat develops diarrhoea, vomiting and jaundice (yellowing of the visible membranes such as the gums and the whites of the eye).

The dry form of FIP

There is no fluid accumulation in the dry form of FIP. Instead, individual organs are attacked, such as the kidney, liver or pancreas. Signs depend on which organ(s) is affected and can include vomiting, diarrhoea, abdominal pain and abortion. Diagnosis can be difficult as FIP can mimic other diseases. Blood tests might be necessary to help with diagnosis. Post-mortem examination of affected organs by a diagnostic laboratory is the only way to get a definite diagnosis.

Treatment

There is no effective treatment at present. Supportive treatment such as fluids, multivitamins, force feeding and antibiotics will prolong life, but usually the cat will die in six weeks or less.

No preventive vaccine is yet available.

FATAL

Q   *Once the disease has been in the household, can it be eliminated so that other cats are not at risk?*

Yes. The virus is easily killed by most disinfectants and does not persist for long outside the cat's body. If you have lost a cat through FIP you could safely introduce another after a few weeks.

Q   *Why are some cats so severely affected and others unaffected?*

We are not sure. One important factor is that, in many cases of FIP, the cat's immune system had been suppressed by some other condition, such as feline leukaemia virus (discussed below).

FIP is more common in young cats (younger than three years old) and is more likely to occur in cat colonies than in individually housed cats. This is presumably because the virus is fragile and cannot survive away from the cat for long, so it persists better if there are many potential victims in one area.

ENTERIC CORONAVIRUS INFECTION

Feline enteric coronavirus infection (FECV) is a viral disease related to FIP, but the course is mild and only rarely severe or fatal. Usual signs are a mild fever, perhaps vomiting, and diarrhoea for two to four days.

FELINE LEUKAEMIA VIRUS

The feline leukaemia virus (or FeLV) can produce severe illness leading to death and might lead to cancer of the lymphatic tissue, such as lymphosarcoma. The disease is not believed to be transmissible to humans.

Signs

The majority of cats show no signs at all. Tests show that in various countries from 30% up to 70% of the adult cat population has been exposed to FeLV. Of these, a few (about 2% or 3%) become carriers and will shed the virus intermittently for years or until their own deaths from the disease.

In the minority of cats that do become ill, the signs are variable, but may include:

* Fever.
* Malaise (lethargy, weakness, physical depression).
* Swollen glands.
* Blood changes—a drop in the number of red and white blood cells.

Death can occur at this stage, although most cats appear to make a recovery. Some cats do in fact make a complete recovery. This is more likely if the signs of illness were only mild.

The sinister aspect of FeLV is that some cats remain persistently infected. The presence of the virus predisposes them to seemingly unrelated diseases, or the cat might experience a recurrence of the original signs. Of persistently infected cats, 70% die within 18 months.

The second stage of feline leukaemia follows a variable period of months to years during which the cat seems normal. Then one of several conditions manifests itself, usually resulting in death. Cancer and infections are the two most common, and are discussed below. Other conditions are also possible because the cat's immune system is severely compromised.

Cancer

The cancer might be a leukaemia (a malignant disease of the white blood cells) or lymphosarcoma (a malignancy involving lymph nodes). The lymph nodes are situated in strategic sites throughout the body. Their role is to filter the body fluids, or lymph, before it is returned to the bloodstream. Lymph tissue includes tonsils, adenoids, thymus, spleen and multiple other 'nodes' in the body cavities, limbs and intestines.

The bone marrow is vital in production of red and white blood cells. It is absolutely vital in resistance to disease, but it is suppressed by FeLV injection. Because of the progressive incapacitation of the immune system, a wide variety of diseases that would normally be overpowered are able to flourish. The most common of these are mouth infections, but other conditions, such as feline infectious peritonitis and feline infectious anaemia, could occur. Many infections that would otherwise be mild are severe, even fatal.

Infection

The virus is shed in most body secretions—blood, saliva, urine, faeces and even tears. It is *not* highly contagious, so prolonged intimate contact, such as mutual grooming and sharing of litter trays, is usually needed for infection to occur. Bite wounds, however, are a possibility for contagion. Most infected queens are infertile. If kittens are born they usually die due to weakness or an Fe.LV-related disease.

Siamese and Burmese are more susceptible than most breeds.

Prevention
Ask your vet about the availability and effectiveness of vaccine.

FELINE IMMUNODEFICIENCY VIRUS

Sometimes called feline AIDS, feline immunodeficiency virus (FIV) is caused by a type of virus closely related to the virus that causes human HIV infection. FIV is not transmissible to humans nor to any other species.

The main route of infection appears to be through bite wounds. The highest infection rates are therefore among males in areas of high feline population density. As long as they do not fight (bite), close and frequent contact between cats living together is unlikely to result in infection. The role of biting and blood-sucking insects in transmission is uncertain.

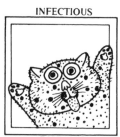

INFECTIOUS

DISEASES

Signs
There are two stages. The first occurs about four weeks after infection but is often so mild the owner fails to notice it. This is a slight

fever, lasting about a week, with swelling of the lymph nodes (which might last several months). Other signs are non-specific but might include lethargy and loss of appetite. In a very few cases the cat may become seriously ill and even die from complications, such as overwhelming bacterial infections.

The second stage is gradual in onset and occurs from months to years later. Most victims are older than 5 years by this stage. Their immune system has gradually become ineffective—unable to cope with its vital role in repelling infection. Viruses and bacteria that would ordinarily be destroyed become real threats, resulting in damage to any or many organs. Sometimes the first suspicion of the disease is that a relatively innocuous infection, such as an abscess or wound, fails to heal despite treatment.

Signs of the second stage vary, but about half of FIV-infected cats develop mouth lesions, such as ulcers or gum inflammation. Many have eye and nasal discharges, perhaps chronic diarrhoea, weight loss, skin infections, anaemia, urinary tract disease and many other possible complications. A few develop changes in personality or habits.

Diagnosis

Diagnosis of FIV is by blood test. Any cat with chronic, poorly responsive disease might be suspected as FIV positive.

RABIES

Rabies is the most feared disease in cats as it can affect people. Once signs develop it is often fatal in humans. Rabies is a viral disease that can affect any warm-blooded animal, but it is most common in carnivores (meat eaters) such as wolves, foxes, skunks and bats.

FATAL

TRANSMITTED

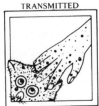

TO HUMANS

The saliva of an infected animal is loaded with the rabies virus, and infection can occur through broken skin or in open wounds or by inhalation of the virus, for example, in a cave infested with rabid bats. Most infections occur through bites. One of the sinister effects of the virus is to produce in many of its victims the desire to attack and bite. When another animal is bitten by the rabid animal the virus is injected into the victim's body, where it seeks out the nervous system and travels slowly up the spinal cord to the brain.

Signs

After the infecting bite, the virus 'incubates' in the cat's body for up to 6 months. Normally only 2–8 weeks pass before signs of the disease start. There are then three further stages.

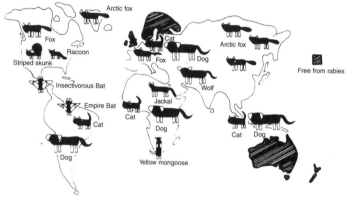

Distribution of rabies: illustrated on the map are species that are particularly important in the spread of rabies in those areas.

The first sign is often a personality change—the timid cat might become very affectionate, or the normally placid and affectionate cat becomes irritable or shy. Usually the cat becomes apprehensive and hides away, often showing a dislike of bright light and noise. In two days or less the cat's condition progresses to the next two stages—first, one of increased excitability (the 'furious' form) followed by the last stage, a state of developing paralysis (the 'dumb' form). The furious form can last up to four days, and the cat is extremely dangerous during this period. Most hide away, but, if disturbed, will attack viciously and persistently. Attacks can be triggered by sudden movements or noise. The 'dumb' form follows. The cat becomes progressively paralysed. Paralysis starts in the hind legs and gradually ascends towards the head.

Death is inevitable and usually occurs within five days of the first signs. It is rare for cats to survive more than 10 days. Some cats do not appear to undergo the 'furious' stage and go directly into the 'dumb' phase.

Treatment

Immediate treatment of a cat known or suspected to have been exposed to rabies will give a good chance of survival. However, once signs have developed the cat has no chance—death is inevitable. Any treatment must be carried out by a vet, and it will probably include antiserum and vaccination.

The World Health Organisation strongly recommends that all unvaccinated cats with rabies be destroyed immediately because of the extreme risk to humans and other animals.

In areas presently free of rabies any cat suspected of having the disease would be taken into isolation by the authorities and stringent tests carried out.

Vaccination

Some countries are free from rabies due to strict quarantine laws, aided by geographical isolation from infected areas. Britain, Australia, Hawaii, New Zealand and parts of Scandinavia are free at present. In these areas vaccination is usually illegal as vaccination can interfere with testing for the disease in the event of an outbreak.

VACCINATION

Where rabies is present (i.e. most of the world) vaccination gives good protection. In some countries vaccination is mandatory. Vaccination can be started at 3 months of age and an annual booster is recommended.

BOOSTER

Q *When is an infected cat first dangerous to other animals or humans?*

The cat's saliva is infectious even before signs start—usually for 24 hours. The cat is then infectious until its death.

Q *What should be done if a person is bitten by a rabid animal?*

Any person bitten or scratched by an animal known to have rabies, or bitten by any animal in an area where rabies is known to exist, should seek immediate medical attention, but first:
- Flush the wound thoroughly—use plenty of soap, and liberally flush and rinse afterwards.
- Then apply an antiseptic to the wound—e.g. tincture or iodine or cetrimide.

TOXOPLASMOSIS

TRANSMITTED

TO HUMANS

Toxoplasmosis is extremely common in cats and in people. Toxoplasmosis is transmissible to humans. Pregnant women especially should beware. At least a third of all cats in the USA and UK are estimated to have been infected at some stage of their lives. In the vast majority of cases infection results in no apparent disease. It is only rarely that toxoplasmosis causes illness in cats. Its major significance is as a health hazard to humans.

Toxoplasmosis is caused by a minute parasite called *toxoplasma gondii* (a protozoan). The cat is the key to its lifecycle, but it can infect any warm-blooded animal.

By far the most common form in the cat is asymptomatic (i.e. there is infection, but no apparent sign of disease). These asymptomatic cats also present a hazard to humans as they still pass out millions of toxoplasma oocysts in the droppings over a period of 1–2 weeks. After only 1–2 days these oocysts become capable of infecting other animals or humans.

The less common forms of toxoplasmosis in the cat are the following two syndromes: acute generalised infection and chronic generalised infection.

Acute generalised infection

This form is more common in young cats and can even be acquired before birth if the queen is infected during pregnancy. The course is short—only about 2 weeks. If a vital organ is severely damaged the cat will die.

Signs
- Fever, loss of appetite, breathing difficulty.
- Jaundice.
- Occasionally diarrhoea and vomiting.
The heart might be damaged.

Chronic generalised infection

This form is more likely to affect older cats, and the course can take many months. First the cat has an intermittent fever, possibly with vomiting, diarrhoea and breathing difficulty. Other signs develop slowly and depend on which organs become involved. They include:

- Nervous signs: If the brain is affected there might be signs such as loss of balance, convulsions, blindness.
- Eye disease: Permanent damage, even blindness, can result from damage to the retina, iris or cornea.
- Heart disease: Including irregular beat or even heart failure.
- Anaemia: Cat tires easily. Might have pale gums.
- Abortion of kittens or birth of weak or dying kittens.

Treatment

Treatment is not always advisable due to the public health aspects (see later). If treatment is commenced it can be quite successful although it only inhibits or controls the disease until the cat develops its own immunity. Any brain or eye damage that occurs before treatment is commenced will be permanent.

Prevention

These recommendations will require some effort on your part, but when the risks of acquiring toxoplasmosis are high, for example, during early pregnancy, then they should be adhered to.

- Only feed your cat with canned food, dry food or food that has been frozen at -20°C for several days.
- Any meat fed to your cat (which has not been frozen) should be cooked well. Cut the meat before cooking to allow better heat penetration.
- Cats should not be allowed to hunt or scavenge. This is not always possible. At least vigorously control vermin, such as mice and rats, as they are a potent source of infection.

Toxoplasma infection of humans

Toxoplasmosis is one of the most common infections found in people throughout the world. In countries like the USA, UK and Australia, 40% – 50% of the population have been infected. In parts of France the figure is 95%. Only Antarctica is free. Toxoplasmosis is especially common in:

- People who eat raw or undercooked meat.
- People who handle meat, e.g. butchers.
- Persons in contact with soil, such as gardeners.
- Children playing in inadequately covered sandpits.
- Persons who fail to empty their cat's litter trays frequently enough.

Signs

Most toxoplasmosis infections in humans result in no signs at all, or in only mild signs of disease. The usual symptoms of patients who do present themselves to a doctor are tiredness, a low-grade fever, swollen lymph nodes and muscle pains. In one study in Great Britain 7% of all patients with swollen lymph nodes had toxoplasmosis. That is a surprisingly large number.

The most serious form of toxoplasmosis in humans occurs when a woman is infected during pregnancy. One sad statistic is that in Europe between 1% and 6% of all babies born are affected by toxoplasmosis. If a mother is infected during pregnancy there is about a 40% chance that the baby will become infected. Of these babies about 15% will be seriously affected. Infection during pregnancy can cause spontaneous abortion (miscarriage), stillbirth or deformities in the child, including mild to severe mental retardation and blindness.

Care must be taken to avoid toxoplasma infection during pregnancy. It is worth repeating here that most toxoplasma infections cause no problems. But the unborn child is especially at risk.

Prevention

All women of childbearing age should know these recommendations.

- Pregnant women should avoid eating raw or undercooked meat. They should be careful of even handling raw meat: better to wear gloves or at least wash your hands thoroughly afterwards.
- Avoid introducing a new cat, especially a young one, to a household where a pregnant woman is present.
- Cat litter trays can be dangerous but are safe if cleaned daily as toxoplasma oocysts do not become infective for at least a day after being passed. To be safe, litter boxes can then be disinfected with hydrogen peroxide, ammonia, sodium hydroxide or strong acid. Flushing with boiling water is adequate if

Litter trays should be cleaned out daily to minimise the danger of toxoplasmosis

done thoroughly. Preferably someone other than the pregnant woman should clean the litter tray.
- Wear gloves when gardening. Once the soil is infected the toxoplasma oocysts can remain potent for up to a year.

- Children's sandboxes should be covered when not in use as they are a favourite spot for cats to use as a toilet.

TETANUS

Cats are about 1500 times more resistant to tetanus than horses, so cases are rare. Tetanus is caused by a bacteria called *clostridium tetani* that lives in the soil. Infection occurs when animals suffer a deep puncture wound that is contaminated by soil, faeces or putrefying matter harbouring the tetanus bacteria. Signs are a progressive muscle stiffness and spasms, eventually resulting in death.

FELINE INFECTIOUS ANAEMIA

Feline infectious anaemia is a disease that occurs worldwide. It is caused by a tiny parasite that lives on the surface of the cat's red blood cells. This parasite is a rickettsia called *Haemobartinella felis*. It multiplies on the cell and causes blood cells either to rupture or to be destroyed by the cat's spleen, resulting in anaemia. In the USA feline infectious anaemia is responsible for about 10% of all feline anaemia cases treated.

In two-thirds of the cases only a mild anaemia results, but then these cats are prone to relapses if stressed (by another disease or by such events as moving house, a new pet in the family, boarding and so on).

In about a third of cases the cat develops a severe anaemia. In these cats clinical signs include lethargy and physical depression, loss of appetite, pale gums, weight loss, a weak pulse and sometimes a fever. Your vet might detect a swollen spleen.

Treatment with specific antibiotics is usually successful.

COCCIDIOSIS

Coccidiosis is a condition seen mainly in cats kept in crowded, unhygienic conditions such as can occur in some pet shops, markets or catteries. It is caused by the microscopic parasites *isospora felis* or *isospora rivolta*. Rats and mice can be a source of infection, but most transmission is due to contamination of the cat's coat, feet or even food with faeces containing the parasite. When the cat grooms itself or eats, the parasite is ingested.

Signs
Loss of appetite, diarrhoea and weight loss are signs of coccidiosis. A faecal test performed by your vet will be needed for a definite diagnosis. Control of infection is achieved by raising the standard

of hygiene and reducing overcrowding. Soiled areas and utensils such as feeding bowls should be disinfected with alkaline cleansers such as sodium hydroxide or ammonia. The infected cats are given antidiarrhoeal preparations containing sulphonamides.

THE SYSTEMIC MYCOSES OR FUNGAL DISEASES

Fungi occur naturally in soil and organic waste. Infection of cats with fungi is not common, but when it does occur, treatment is often difficult. The development of fungal disease is slow and insidious.

Cryptococcosis

Cryptococcosis is caused by *cryptococcus neoformans*. This fungus is widely distributed. It is a soil organism that finds pigeon droppings especially suitable for growth. Infections are uncommon.

Signs
- Upper respiratory tract: Invasion of the nasal passages produces a thick discharge and partial airway blockages, resulting in noisy or difficult breathing.
- The infection might break through bone into the area around the brain and cause a meningitis.
- In the skin form, cryptococcus produces multiple lumps or nodules on the face or body, which can ulcerate and resemble skin tumours or abscesses.
- In other forms the eyes or the abdominal organs might be infected.

Treatment
Treatment is difficult and can be expensive. Euthanasia is often recommended.

The disease is transmissible to people but this is highly unlikely, unless the person in contact is very old, very young or highly susceptible to infections.

Actinomycoses

Actinomycoses is caused by *actinomyces bovis*. It is a rare infection in cats that can occur after a physical trauma to the nose, plus contamination with soil. Actinomyces causes large, irregularly shaped swellings in, or just under, the skin. Large pockets of pus might form.

Histoplasmosis

Histoplasmosis is caused by *histoplasma capsulatum*. Seen in the central river basins of North America, it is transmitted mainly through starlings' droppings. Spores can be ingested or inhaled. It can cause problems in the lungs (cough, difficult breathing) or the gut (diarrhoea, weight loss), or both.

Blastomycoses

Blastomycoses is caused by *blastomyces dermatides*. Found in central parts of North America. Causes a lung infection. In some cats it might progress to a generalised disease with abscesses under the skin, which rupture and discharge. Lameness and blindness can occur.

Coccidiomycosis

Coccidiomycosis is caused by *coccidiomycosis immitis*. It is found in south-western USA. The main significance of coccidiomycosis is as a respiratory disease of people. The cat can be infected by its owner, producing a mild condition of the lungs, which might be complicated by bacterial infection. It usually causes the cat little or no distress.

10 TEETH AND MOUTH

The cat is a predator. Its teeth have gradually evolved to suit that role. The cat can use its teeth to hold and kill prey, and then shear meat into pieces small enough to allow swallowing. The cat's food requires little or no chewing to make it digestible. The cat can eat large meals very quickly, gulping it all down—scales, feathers, hair and all.

Cats bite with a chopping up and down action. They are unable to use the side-to-side grinding action that the human jaw is designed to make.

Incisors / Canines Molars

NORMAL TEETH

Kittens have 26 teeth. Adult cats have 30. The mouth is dominated by the four huge canines, designed to hold and kill prey and for defence. The back teeth, or molars, have cusps, or cutting edges, to allow the cat to shear the food into manageable pieces.

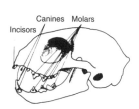

Teething in kittens

The kitten is born without teeth. The first of the temporary or 'milk' teeth emerge at about 2 weeks of age. By the

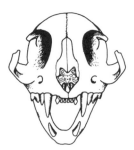

fifth or sixth week the kitten has 26 teeth. The permanent teeth start to emerge at around 4 months of age, or a little later. It takes another 2 months for all the teeth to emerge. The roots of the temporary teeth break down, and the tooth is pushed out by the emerging permanent tooth. During this period of change the kitten will experience occasional episodes of tenderness around the gums, and might therefore be reluctant to eat. This discomfort is transient. There is no need for concern or medication.

Retained temporary teeth

Sometimes the permanent tooth will grow up next to the temporary tooth and fail to dislodge it. These retained teeth can interfere with the correct alignment of the permanent teeth, therefore it is best to allow your vet to inspect the mouth. The vet might decide to remove the offending temporary teeth because food and debris can be trapped alongside retained teeth, causing foul breath, sore gums and a reluctance to eat on the tender side.

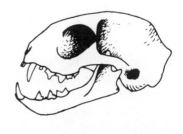

The most commonly retained teeth are the canines.

Overcrowding of teeth

Some short-nosed breeds, such as the Persian, Colour Point or Himalayan, have too short a jaw to fit in all the teeth comfortably. The resultant overcrowding can cause difficulty eating or

Undershot jaw; overshot jaw

rapid build-up of tartar with consequent gum disease (discussed later in this chapter). In severe cases, your vet might have to remove some teeth to allow the cat to close its mouth comfortably. Cats with badly overcrowded mouths should definitely not be used for breeding.

The lower jaw of some cats, notably the Persian, can be overlong ('sow' mouth) or too short ('parrot' mouth). The upper and lower teeth of these cats do not meet correctly. This results in abnormal wear, especially of the incisors. If you intend to buy a

Persian kitten you should inspect its 'bite' before purchase and so avoid the dental problems associated with an abnormal jaw.

Signs

Affected cats affected by mouth pain or disease will show some of the following signs:

- Drooling of saliva.
- Bad breath.
- Reluctance or inability to eat.
- Lip smacking.
- Pawing of mouth.
- Open mouth (the tongue will protrude a little as a result).

MOUTH ULCERS

The most common cause of mouth ulcers is feline respiratory disease (see chapter 9). The tongue is the most common site of the ulcers but the gums and throat can also be involved. Kidney disease can lead to mouth ulcers.

Corrosive chemicals such as alkalis and strong acids will burn and ulcerate the mouth. Cats almost never sample such chemicals willingly, but they could pick them up while grooming themselves or when licking contaminated paws.

Treatment

The ulcers themselves heal rapidly once the underlying cause has been remedied. When the ulcer is fresh, the mouth will

Bad breath can be a sign of dental disease

be sensitive, and the cat will probably be reluctant to eat or drink. After 1–3 days the cat will usually start to accept a little food. Offer small chunks of meat or little small, soft balls of food. These can be quickly swallowed without much effort. Food and drink is less irritating to a sensitive mouth if served warm—at about blood temperature.

Multivitamins help to stimulate the appetite and to speed up healing. Vitamin C and the B group are especially recommended.

BROKEN TEETH

Car accidents or fights can result in broken or chipped teeth. Unless the root is exposed, these teeth rarely cause the cat any concern, and no treatment is needed. If the tooth is broken flush with the gum line or if it is worrying the cat, the sensitive inner part of the tooth has probably been exposed. Infection might enter. Let your vet inspect the damaged tooth. It might be necessary to remove the remaining tooth and root under a general anaesthetic.

OLD CATS AND WORN TEETH

As cats age, some teeth might be lost through gum disease or through deterioration of the jaw bone. In some disease states—for example, chronic kidney disease—calcium is leached from the bones and the teeth become unstable in their sockets and might fall out.

Cats with only a few teeth or even no teeth can cope quite happily as long as you feed them soft foods, small chunks or balls of food small enough to be swallowed without chewing.

Q   *Can you tell a cat's age by the teeth?*

Not accurately. Once a cat's permanent teeth have erupted they do not have a consistent variation with age, unlike the horse's teeth, which change at fairly predictable intervals.

JAW FRACTURES

Jaw fractures can result from knocks, kicks, car accidents or similar traumas. The most frequent cause is a fall from a height. The cat's lower jaw thumps on to the ground and might break—usually in the middle of the mandible.

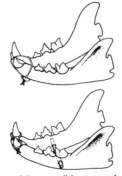

Some of the possible ways of repairing a fractured jaw. The wires and/or pins are removed after the fracture has healed

Treatment

Most jaw fractures respond well to wiring or pinning. The patient will usually be able to eat and drink comfortably with these pieces of hardware in place while healing progresses. See chapter 7, 'Bones and Joints'.

FOREIGN BODIES IN THE MOUTH

Pieces of bone, fish hooks, needles and other foreign bodies can become accidentally lodged in the cat's mouth.

The cat's tongue is covered with small horny barbs or papillae. These project backwards towards the throat and turn the cat's tongue into an efficient rasp, which can be used to remove flesh from bones when eating and to remove loose hair from the coat while grooming. If a cat is playing with a thread, these barbs can catch the thread and the cat might be unable to disentangle it. By gulping and moving the tongue, the papillae gradually move the thread back down the throat and it is swallowed. Complications can arise if there is a needle on the other end of the thread. Fortunately, the needle enters blunt-end first.

Many small needles will pass through the cat's bowel without causing harm. Others get caught, and severe discomfort and illness result if the needle penetrates the throat, gullet (oesophagus) or the bowel.

Fish hooks might become caught in the cat's mouth, especially if hooks are unwisely still left baited. If the barb has gone through the lip it is possible to cut the hook in two and remove it relatively painlessly (see 'Objects caught in the mouth' in chapter 2).

TARTAR

In the wild, cats *use* their teeth, and this keeps them clean and healthy. As the cat eats, the biting, tearing and cutting actions have a natural abrasive and cleansing effect on the teeth. Cats fed foods that encourage this mouth exercise rarely have problems with tartar formation. Unfortunately many cats are fed mainly on soft processed foods that require little or no chewing. As a result these cats frequently develop a heavy build-up of tartar on their teeth.

Tartar, or dental calculus, starts as little more than an apparent stain on the teeth, but it can gradually build into huge masses covering the teeth, exposing the roots and loosening the teeth. Bacteria proliferate at the gum margin.

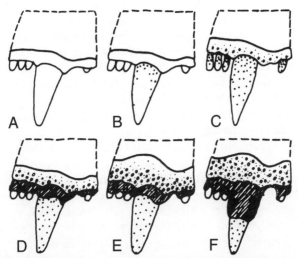

The stages of tartar formation. A. Dental 'plaque' is initially little more than an invisible film; B. C. gradually the plaque is stained and a mineral deposit starts; D. E. F. salts and minerals precipitate and gradually a solid mass forms. The gum is pushed back. Bacterial infections can become established between the tartar mass and the gums.

Signs of tartar build-up
- Foul breath.
- Excessive salivation, perhaps occasionally blood-flecked.
- Pain on eating, or reluctance to chew.
- Pawing at the mouth.
- Sudden dropping of food from the mouth.

If you lift your cat's lips back to expose the molars you can readily see whether tartar is forming. If the gum margins are reddened and inflamed, the cat is probably experiencing some discomfort. Although the build-up of tartar is gradual, taking months or years, the onset of signs of discomfort can be quite sudden.

Treatment
If the tartar has built to a formidable mass it is best to have your vet thoroughly clean the teeth under a general anaesthetic. Damaged

teeth can be removed at the same time. Although cats rarely develop cavities in their teeth, damage to the tooth roots might be so extensive that removal of the teeth is necessary.

If tartar formation is only in the early stages, preventive measures may slow or even reverse new formation.

Prevention

Prevention is the best approach to dental disease. A sensible diet is the key. If the cat is fed only soft canned food or minced foods, there is little natural cleaning of the teeth. Instead, food debris accumulates and bacteria can flourish. By feeding chunks or strips of meat or raw chicken wings or raw bones, you will promote the natural abrasion of the tooth surfaces and stimulate a good flow of saliva. Both these actions help to remove debris.

Some cats will even allow their owner to clean their teeth. Using a soft, child's toothbrush or a damp piece of flannel plus a mild abrasive paste. (A mixture of equal parts bicarbonate of soda and table salt is suitable, or you could obtain a commercial preparation from your veterinarian.) It is better to clean only one or two teeth at a session until you have the teeth clean. Later you can keep any new tartar formation under control with a short weekly session encompassing all the teeth. Concentrate on the gum margins of the molars, premolars and canines, as this is where the problem starts.

RODENT ULCER

Rodent ulcers (or *eosinophilic granuloma*) are open sores found primarily on the inside of the cat's upper lip, adjacent to the canine tooth. They sometimes develop in other sites: on the tongue, lips, roof of the mouth or on the skin of the abdomen or inner thigh. The term *rodent* ulcer is misleading. It originated because it was thought these sores were due to infections contracted from mice or rats. Their real cause is still uncertain, but might be associated with an underlying allergic disorder (e.g. flea allergy, food allergy or inhaled allergy).

These sores are usually oval in shape, with a raised edge or border. The affected area is gradually eroded. It becomes red and inflamed, and might bleed intermittently, especially if knocked. Early in its course, the ulcer is small and causes concern to the cat. As it progresses, eating can become uncomfortable, and the cat might lose its appetite, salivate and paw at the mouth.

Treatment

Some cases respond to treatment with drugs. In advanced cases, surgical removal might be contemplated, although it can be deforming.

X-ray treatment, cryo-surgery (deep cold treatment) and injections into and around the sore have been successful in some selected cases. Treatment is not always successful, and recurrence is common.

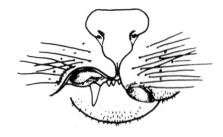

A rodent ulcer is easier to see if you lift the lip back

THE COUGHING CAT

A cough is a defensive reflex designed to clear irritants from the throat or chest. The cough is produced by the violent contraction of the chest and diaphragm, resulting in a blast of air through the windpipe and throat.

The manner in which a cat coughs can present a worrying sight to an owner. A cat cough is less subtle than a human cough, and it appears to come right from the throat. As one cough leads to another, a paroxysm of coughing can develop, inducing many owners to believe erroneously that their cat has something lodged in the throat. Not infrequently, the cat appears to be on the point of vomiting.

A cat that really *does* have an object caught in the throat large enough potentially to obstruct breathing will usually exhibit the following signs:

- Mouth open.
- Gagging.
- Head down, neck extended.
- Pawing at mouth.
- Perhaps blood flecking of saliva.
- Violent expulsive effects with chest.

When the foreign matter is small, such as a fish bone, it can be very difficult to detect. If such an object is suspected and the cat is distressed, it might be necessary to examine the cat under a general anaesthetic.

Many conditions can lead to a cough. The most common are discussed below.

Matter caught in the back of the throat

Hair is a common cause. While grooming, the cat might get a small hairball caught in the pharynx or behind the soft palate. Other matter that might be involved includes grass, pieces of dry food and fish bones.

Tonsilitis

Infection of the tonsils leads to swelling and inflammation, and in some cases to pus formation. Tonsilitis can be one part of a more generalised disease, such as feline respiratory disease (see chapter 9, 'Infectious Diseases').

Lungworm

See chapter 16, 'Heart and Lungs'.

Lung infections

If mucus or other debris is building up in the chest the cat will cough it up in an attempt to clear the airways.

Irritating fumes or dust

Some cats like to sit near heating vents or fan heaters and could breathe in considerable amounts of dust particles blown up from the floor. Other cats might be housed incorrectly where fumes form, for example, a garage. These fumes can irritate the throat and lungs.

Growths in the mouth

Cysts, polyps or even cancerous growths can form in the mouth. If these encroach towards the back of the cat's mouth or throat they can cause coughing.

Allergies

Coughing can be a sign of allergy in a cat. It is referred to as feline asthma.

Treatment

Because coughing has so many possible causes, it is undesirable to try home remedies if the cough is persistent or severe. Fortunately, in most cases, the cough is merely a reflex-clearing mechanism. Even if the cough develops into a short spasm there is usually little cause for concern or need for treatment. However, if the cough is repeated and is distressing the cat, you might be able to relieve it with a little warm mineral oil (2–5 ml) given by the mouth. This breaks up any matter trapped in the back of the cat's throat and helps flush it down to the stomach.

11 THE EAR

A cat's ears are normally held erect and alert, but they can be directionally aligned to gather sound, or flattened in a show of anger. Unlike dogs, most cats have the same basic ear shape, with the exception of the Scottish Fold, which wears its ears folded forward on its head.

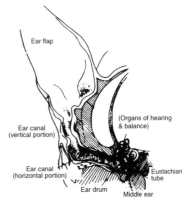

The cat's ear has a long, deep canal where infections or infestation could become established

CLEANING EARS AND ROUTINE TREATMENTS

The car is sensitive about its ears and will resist excessive attention or handling of them. However, it might become necessary to clean or treat the cat's ear, for example, to remove dirt or wax accumulation or to treat an infection. Your vet will supply you with a solution designed specifically to clean a cat's ears, or you can use a wax solvent preparation designed for humans. Some owners find that warm mineral oil is satisfactory. If you can get someone to help hold the cat, the whole procedure is much easier.

A few words of caution: the cat is likely to flick its head and ears, throwing oil and wax about. Be careful that it does not stain valuable clothes or furniture.

When applying medications, gently massage the preparation deep down into the canal

- Hold down the cat's head slightly to one side.
- Instil a few drops of the cleaning or medication preparation deep into the ear canal.
- Massage the preparation down the ear canal deep into the ear.
- Wipe away any excess with damp cotton wool. (*Do not* use cotton buds. They are liable to damage the ear.)

Signs

Some of the following warning signs indicate that your cat has an ear problem:

- Head shaking.
- Head tilted to one side.
- Twitching ear.
- Pawing or scratching at or near the ear.
- Strong or foul smell from the ear.
- Discharge from ear—could be pus, wax or dark discharge.
- Rubbing ear along the ground.

If the deeper structures of the ear are affected, the delicate structures involved with balance can become involved. The signs could then include:

- Head tilted to one side.
- Loss of balance—the cat could stagger, especially when turning, and might even fall. The cat's 'righting reflex' is extremely sensitive, but it could be lost if the inner ear is affected. Normally, even if held upside down only a few centimetres from the floor, then released, the cat will turn and twist in a fraction of a second to land square on its feet. When this reflex is interfered with,

the cat will be unable to climb or jump with any certainty, and might be reluctant to move about.

- Circling in one direction. If only one ear is affected, the cat will tend to walk in circles. If the right ear is affected, the cat will circle only to the right, and vice versa if the left ear is affected.

EAR MITES

The most common ear infection of cats is infestation by the tiny ear mite *otodectes cynotis*. This is especially common in kittens. These mites feed on the delicate lining of the ear canal, causing irritation and discomfort and the production of a dark brown wax discharge. This wax is readily seen if you shine a penlight into the ear canal. In some cases it oozes from the ear, where it dries and forms irritating crusts.

Mild infestations usually do not concern the cat. If the infestation is heavy the cat could become acutely uncomfortable. By scratching at the ears the cat might inflict further damage in its efforts to relieve the irritation.

Large amount of very dark wax in the ears suggests ear mite infection.

Treatment

Be gentle and careful whenever you handle your cat's ears. Read the section on cleaning ears and routine treatments above. A suitable insecticidal preparation can be purchased from your vet. These preparations generally have an ear wax solvent included in their formula, so separate wax solvents are not required.

The most common reason for lack of success in treating ear mite infestation is not continuing the treatment for long enough. You might have to continue treatment for 3 weeks. Or, treat twice daily for one week, cease treatment for the

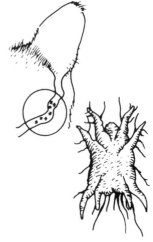

Ear mites can cause irritation and discomfort

next week, then treat again the third week. This kills the mites that have hatched out after the first week's treatment. Always treat both ears and all other cats and dogs in the household. Ear mites are easily transmitted between animals (although fortunately they will not infest humans). Because some of the mites live on the cat's body as well, it is worthwhile to treat the cat simultaneously with an insecticidal powder or rinse.

OTHER PARASITES

Another mite sometimes found is *notodres cati*. Unlike the common ear mite, which lives on the surface, this mite burrows into the skin. It produces intense irritation, raised lumps in the skin and dry, crusty flaky skin patches.

Notodres cati can affect cats and rabbits. It is not common, but when it occurs it is highly infectious.

Treatment
Rinse the affected areas with 0.5% malathion (25 ml malathion diluted with 2 litres water) or 2½% lime sulphur. Repeat the treatment once weekly for at least 6 weeks.

EAR INFECTIONS

The ear canal can become infected with a variety of organisms, including bacteria, fungi and yeasts. The name given to an infection of the ear canal is *otitis externa*, although many people refer to it as 'canker'.

Bacteria, fungi and yeasts are present in the normal ear canal. The cat's immune system is capable of resisting any build-up of these organisms under normal circumstances. Sometimes the environment within the ear canal changes, providing conditions suitable for these germs to multiply. Such conditions can occur if wax builds up excessively in the ear, or if the ear is bitten or scratched by another cat or by the cat itself while scratching at an irritation within the ear, such as mites or a grass seed.

Signs
A foul-smelling exudate builds up in the ear canal and could spill out to matt down the hair at the base of the ear. *Otitis externa* can cause severe damage to the ear canal, and if neglected could penetrate the ear drum, leading to damage of the delicate middle and inner ear. This results in pain, loss of balance and even deafness.

Treatment

The treatment depends on what particular organisms are involved. It might be necessary to send samples to be cultured by a veterinary pathologist to identify the agent involved and to determine which drugs will be most effective in treating it.

In bacterial infections, antibiotic ear ointments are usually prescribed. For yeast and fungal infections a different range of drugs is required. The precise choice of treatment should be left to your vet.

In severe or painful cases, or where a foreign body such as a grass seed is present, your vet might suggest that the ears be thoroughly cleaned while the cat is under a general anaesthetic.

Do not persist with ineffective home treatments for ear infections. Permanent damage could result.

FOREIGN BODIES IN EARS

Foreign bodies such as grass seeds or awns could be caught in a cat's ear. They gradually work their way into the ear canal. Sometimes children poke things such as sticks into a cat's ears. If you see a foreign body in the ear and can pull it out easily with tweezers, or similar, then do so. However, if the object has penetrated deeply or resists a gentle pull, then leave it and consult your vet. The ear is too delicate to risk forcing it.

Do not persist in vain attempts to remove objects from cats' ears as this can result in severe ear damage.

SUNBURNED EARS

Cats with white ears that live in sunny climates are liable to sunburn of the ears. This can lead, in time, to cancer of the ears. White skin lacks the protective pigments that prevent damage by the sun's ultraviolet rays. Unfortunately many white cats love to bask in the sun as they do not get as hot as dark-coloured cats. Damage can occur to any area of white skin but is most common on the ear tips, eyelids and around the nose.

Sunburn can lead to ear cancer

Signs

Signs of severe skin damage can take years to appear. The ear might appear to heal during winter only to flare up again a little more severely each summer. The first sign is a red, flaky area around the rim of the ear, followed by a slight curling of the ear tip. Gradually, small scales appear, and the owner might mistakenly believe the cat has been scratched. These sores progress to become dark scabs with raw, swollen areas beneath, which bleed profusely when the scab is knocked off. In time, the condition progresses to a cancer known as squamous cell carcinoma. The ear tip ulcerates, and the erosive, destructive cancerous process begins to destroy the ear. The ear becomes thickened, inflamed and angry looking.

Treatment

Once the first signs are recognised, the best treatment is to avoid any further exposure to strong sunlight. If possible, the cat should be kept indoors between 10 a.m. and 4 p.m. in the hot summer months. This might be impracticable. In these cases, coat the ear tips with an ultraviolet blockout cream, available from chemists. A children's preparation is preferable to adult preparations, and the most effective types are those that are absorbed into the skin rather than just sitting on the surface as the cat will remove the latter during routine grooming. Zinc cream preparations that resist washing off are available.

Some owners have had success using a black felt non-toxic marker pen once a week to provide artificial pigment on the ear margins.

If the condition has been neglected and cancer has started, surgery is usually required. The affected part of the ear is amputated. Other treatments include cryosurgery (deep cold treatment of the damaged tissue) or X-ray therapy. Therapy using drugs is only of limited use at present.

BLOOD BLISTER OF THE EAR

A large swelling under the skin of the ear is probably a blood blister of the ear or aural haematoma. It is formed when a blood vessel bursts and bleeds into the area between the ear cartilage and the outer skin. It might be as the result of a fight or constant rubbing and scratching, or head shaking due to ear mites or other infections.

A blood blister is usually not particularly painful, but if it is not drained

Aural haematoma

the ear will become distorted and scarred during healing, resulting in a 'cauliflower ear'.

Treatment
Your vet will drain the fluid from the ear, usually while the cat is under a general anaesthetic. The ear is then splinted so that it heals in its original shape with the minimum of distortion by scar tissue.

INFECTIONS BEYOND THE EAR DRUM

Infections that involve the middle and inner ear (*otitis media* and *otitis interna*) are potentially very serious. The delicate hearing apparatus can be permanently damaged, resulting in deafness. In addition, the organs of balance are situated in the inner ear (the semi-circular canals). If inflammation or infection is present the cat might lose its sense of balance.

Signs
In mild cases the cat will only have a head tilt, holding the affected side down. As the condition progresses the cat might develop a tendency to circle in one direction and balance is progressively lost: at first the cat will stagger or stumble, but this progresses to a total inability to stand upright, so that the cat remains crouched down and is reluctant to move.

Treatment
The treatment depends on the cause. If a bacterial infection is responsible then antibiotics, perhaps in combination with surgery to drain the pus, might be successful, but in some cases the damage to the nerves is permanent.

In general, early treatment often gives a good chance of recovery. However, if the damage is severe or treatment is delayed, the cat could be left with permanent hearing impairment or with a head tilt. This head tilt often becomes less obvious with time as the cat adapts to compensate for the permanently damaged nerves.

DEAFNESS

Deafness can be present from birth (termed 'congenital' deafness). This is the case with most blue-eyed white cats. This deafness is due to a genetic defect, and there is no treatment. White cats with one blue eye and one eye of another colour are usually deaf only in the ear next to the blue eye.

Other causes of deafness include:

- Ear infections that are untreated or fail to respond to treatment can result in deafness.
- Drug reactions: some drugs, for example, the antibiotic dihydrostreptomycin, cause deafness.
- Old age: many cats become progressively deaf with advancing age. The reason for this is not known, nor is there any effective treatment.

12 THE EYE

The cat has the largest eye compared with body weight of any of the domestic species. Limited white of the eye is visible when we look at they eye of the cat. Most of what we see is the eye windows (or cornea). The cat's large cornea allows a wide field of vision and allows maximum light to enter the eye for night vision.

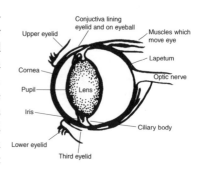

A cat does not see close objects in focus as we do. This is because the cat cannot change the shape of its lens and therefore cannot focus the image sharply. To sharpen the image the cat narrows the pupils into slit-like openings.

CHARACTERISTICS OF CATS' EYES

What gives colour to the eye?

Cats' eyes come in a variety of colours. This colour is due to pigment in the iris. Occasionally a cat is born with eyes of different colours. The most common eye colours are yellow and green; others include orange, blue and pink eyes. Pigment in the iris is needed to protect the retina from too much light. Lack of pigment (blue eye) can mean less protection against bright light. Blue eyes in Siamese can be associated with a thin, underdeveloped iris. A thin blue iris is not as good for the cat's comfort as a darker eye.

What does a cat see?

The shape of a cat's eye is such that the cat is better able to detect moving, rather than stationary prey. A cat detecting movement out of the corner of its eye will turn its head rapidly to bring the object into better view. A cat might fail to see a mouse sitting still against a grey background, but if the mouse runs it stimulates the retina. The cat can accurately pounce on the moving target. It is doubtful whether cats have much ability to recognise objects at a distance. Rather than hunt like a dog or fox, cats prefer to lie in wait, springing at their prey when it is within striking distance.

Does a cat see at night?

While the cat's night vision is very much better than that of people, night vision is comparatively short-range. No eyes can penetrate total darkness. The cat's night vision is aided by a special reflecting shield at the back of the eye behind the retina (the tapetum). The tapetum is responsible for eye shine in the dark and reflects light so that the eye can be stimulated by low intensities of light.

While the cat cannot focus well, the extreme mobility of the pupil offers the cat good vision in greatly differing lights. It is remarkable that cats are so readily adapted to night vision yet can enjoy good day vision as well. Most creatures of the dark, such as owls and moles, have very poor vision in bright light.

Colour vision in the cat

The cat's eyes have adapted to suit its specific needs as a hunter. There is little need for a cat to be able to distinguish colour, so its not surprising to find that its colour vision is limited. It was once thought that cats had no colour vision at all, but experiments have shown that they can distinguish some colours from each other. Blue is probably their best colour, and they appear to be able to distinguish various hues or shades of blue from each other. They are probably red blind, and have only a limited ability to distinguish green from blue.

BLINDNESS

A blind cat can cope so well in its own home that it is difficult to believe that it is nearly or totally blind. This happens if blindness is gradual. Sudden blindness, as might occur in diabetic cats, is not tolerated well. The cat might, however, bump into furniture in a dark room or move slowly about, nose down, feeling its way with its whiskers. A blind cat might misjudge when jumping up, although some (remarkably) can still jump a fence.

If you suspect your cat is blind, it should be examined by a veterinarian.

Blind cats can manage well in their own environment. Long whiskers help. Some blind cats will even jump the back fence

Coping with blindness

A blind cat usually copes very well, especially if the onset of blindness has been slow and the sense of smell and hearing are intact. A blind cat is helped by:

- Familiar environment (do not move the furniture).
- A keen sense of smell and hearing (have the ears checked).
- Less need of vision than people.
- Another cat or dog in the household acting as a 'guide dog'.
- Leaving whiskers long.

If you suspect blindness keep the cat indoors until the eyes are checked or it might be run over or become lost.

EYELID INJURIES

Most eyelid injuries are serious. Very swollen eyelids can hide a badly damaged eyeball. Keep the eyeball moist (see the section on 'Dry Eye') and hurry to the vet. Extensive lid injury may require plastic surgery. When the eyelids cannot cover the eyeball and sweep tears over the cornea, the eyeball becomes dry. Damage to the eye follows rapidly. If the eyelids cannot cover the eyeball, keep the eye constantly wet while hurrying to the vet.

Stye

A stye is a small boil or abscess at the eyelid edge. It might need to be lanced and drained by your vet. Antibiotics are often needed.

Inflammation of the eyelids

Skin diseases can affect eyelid skin. Sunlight makes inflammation much worse so keep the patient inside. *Beware:* inflamed eyelids due to injury, infection or ringworm may cause an inflamed eye.

EYELID DISEASES OF NEWBORN KITTENS

The eyelids of the newborn kitten remain closed until about the tenth day. Opening of the eyes much before this can lead to blindness later. If the eyes open prematurely you should:

- Keep the eyes moist. Artificial tears are ideal, but clean tap water will do.
- Seek veterinary help immediately. Your vet might have to suture the eyelids together.

Bulging eyelids

Bulging, closed eyelids in a newborn kitten mean an eye infection and can lead to loss of the eye. *Beware:* the infection might not be obvious, showing only as a swollen eyelid or a little pus at the corner of the eye. Swollen eyelids in a newborn kitten is an emergency. The eyelids must be surgically opened at once. If you cannot see the vet immediately, gently ease open the closed lids with a toothpick to allow pus to drain out. After opening, apply antibiotic ointment continually to control the infection and keep the eyes lubricated. The eyelids must not be allowed to stick together until the infection has cleared.

EYE DISEASES PRESENT AT BIRTH

Diseases seen at birth (congenital diseases) are not necessarily inherited. Some diseases seen at birth are also inherited. Some inherited diseases are not evident at birth but develop some time later.

Squint

A squint (turned eyes or crossed eyes) is most commonly seen in Siamese and is probably inherited. The cause of squint is due to maldevelopment of the visual pathways, that is, the nerve pathways from the eye to brain. Slight squint is not obvious. Use the slit-like

Cross eyes (squint) occur when the nerve pathways from the eyeball are abnormal. We should not accept this as 'normal' and should only breed from cats free of this disorder

pupils in broad daylight to help you examine for slight turning of the eyeball. Compare the pupils to see if the eyes are slightly turned towards the nose. Vision is present, appears adequate but is impaired.

Small eye

Some kittens are born with a very small eye. This is due to prematurely arrested development of the eyeball. A small eye means a vision defect.

Eyelids fail to open

If the newborn kitten's lids remain closed after 12 days of age, this is a danger sign. Failure of the eyes to open normally is usually associated with infection (neonatal conjuctivitis), which can cause blindness.

ACQUIRED EYE DISEASES

Bulging/prominent/'big' eyes

Prominent eyes can be caused by injury, infection, glaucoma or, more rarely, cancer. Infections that spread to the eyeball from the sinus also might cause the eye to bulge. Protrusion of the eyeball prevents eyelid closure. Lightly tap the corners of the eyelids with your finger to check whether blinking can cause the lids to meet over a big eyeball. Seek veterinary attention at once if the eyelids cannot cover the eyeball. While you are rushing to the vet, keep the prolapsed eyeball wet by squirting saline from a syringe on to the eye.

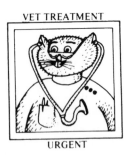

VET TREATMENT

URGENT

A growth behind the eyeball is another cause of eye protrusion. The majority are malignant and respond poorly to treatment. You will notice a gradual bulging of the eye, which gets worse over a matter of weeks.

Untreated chronic glaucoma can lead to increased size of the eye and protrusion. Chronic increase in pressure (glaucoma) enlarges the eyeball. This is seen mostly in old cats. The lens inside the eyeball becomes dislocated and damages delicate internal structures of the eye. Do not confuse a big eye with a big pupil—ask your vet to show you the difference.

Eye closed since birth

A kitten's eye closed since birth can be due to adhesions of the eyelids to the eyeball. Surgery might be helpful.

Sunken eye

The eyeball can recede when there is loss of substance in the fat 'cushion' behind the eye, for example, in dehydration or rapid weight loss (enophthalmos). Moreover, behind the eyeball there is a muscle that, when it goes into spasm, can pull the eye back into its socket. This might occur with a painful injury. Damage to a nerve in the head, neck or chest can result in a sunken eyeball and a small pupil (Horner's syndrome). As the eye sinks back, the third eyelid becomes more obvious, and there is an accumulation of mucus on the corner of the eye.

Eyelids held closed/squinting

Spasm of the eye-closing muscles (blepharospasm) is induced by pain such as from foreign materials in the eye. Irritation causes tightening of the muscles of the eyelids, closing the eye and rolling the eyelids in against the cornea. Hair on the lids rolls in and rubs against the eyeball, causing further pain.

Inflamed/irritated eyelids

Inflammation of the eyelids (*blepharitis*) is common because the eyelids are frequently injured during cat fights. Scratches can easily become infected. This leads to itching and crust formation and the accumulation of pus and debris on the eyelids.

Inflammation of the eyelids often accompanies conjuctivitis. This can be due to many causes ranging from bacterial infection to mange mites and ringworm. The condition is made worse by self-mutilation. Hair is lost, and the lid becomes thickened and ulcerated. *Note:*

- Skin ointments prescribed to treat the area around the eye must not be placed in the eye.
- Self-mutilation can be a problem.
- Keep the patient out of the sun.

Tuberculosis of the eyelids

In some countries the eyelids of the cat can be affected by bovine TB. Lumps (tubercles) are seen on the eyelids, and usually the cat has a generalised tuberculosis. With primary infection in the throat region, the lids become affected because the cat cleans its face with its paws. The affected cat is a health risk to people.

Eye rolled inward

This condition (entropion) occurs as an hereditary defect in some Persian cats, but can occur in any cat as a result of scarring of the lower lid, for example, following a bout of severe infection or laceration of the eyelid. The lower eyelid of old cats rolls in when the eyeball sinks in too far in its socket. This may be due to loss of a fat pad at the back of the eye. Some cats have entropion because the eyelids are too big.

To diagnose entropion, look for absence of a lower lid margin. The rolled in lid irritates the eye and causes a watery discharge. The defect can be corrected by surgery.

Tumours

Growths of the eyelid margin should be removed even if they only threaten to irritate the eyeball.

Cancer eye

Cancer eye or squamous cell carcinoma (SCC) is more common in older white cats. SCC typically begins on the lid margin but can occur on the third eyelid or on the eyeball. When it first appears it looks like inflammation and not like a dangerous lump. Sunlight is more likely to damage unpigmented skin. Once the SCC has started, further exposure to sunlight is likely to make the condition worse.

Beware: a sore on the eye of a lightly coloured cat could be a cancer.

THE THIRD EYELID

The third eyelid, or nictitating (winking) membrane, is a protective 'extra' eyelid at the inner corner of each eye, next to the nose. When needed, the third eyelid can sweep across the eyeball like a windscreen wiper to help remove the debris. Several conditions can affect the third eyelid.

Haws

The third eyelid is held in position by very small muscles, and when their nerve supply is disturbed, the third eyelid protrudes. This condition is known as 'haws'. The third eyelid can become more prominent due to many causes—some involving the eye but some due to conditions affecting the whole body. A prominent third eyelid can be due to many causes such as inflammation, adhesions of the third eyelid, intestinal disease, injury to the eye or neck or cancer.

Prominent third eyelids (haws) can mean disease elsewhere in the body or disease of the eye

The third eyelid looks like a 'skin' covering the inner part of the eye, usually about a quarter to a half of the eye being covered. Owners often mistakenly report that their cat has a film covering the eye. Some cases of haws resolve themselves after about eight weeks.

The third eyelid is vital for eye health and should *never* be removed even if it is persistently prominent. If the third eyelid is removed, tear production is reduced and later the eye can become dry and very sick.

Treatment

A prominent third eyelid is usually only one sign that there is eye disease or body disease. A veterinary examination determines the cause.

Pink third eyelid

A pink third eyelid is the one that lacks pigment. Lack of pigment makes it appear prominent as it contrasts with the eyeball behind it. Pink third eyelids can become sunburned. Keep cats with unpigmented eyelids out of summer sun.

CONJUNCTIVITIS

The conjuntiva is a thin membrane that covers and protects the white of the eye and lines the eyelids. It is usually transparent but becomes more obvious when it is inflamed.

Conjunctivitis is the commonest of eye diseases. It is uncomfortable and tends to recur and cause more pain. Typically it does not cause visual loss but, if neglected, can lead to serious discomfort. Conjunctivitis can be cured, but the eyes will become inflamed again whenever they are irritated enough. Avoid the sun or other predisposing factors, such as spraying insecticide, to lessen the chance of relapse.

Conjunctivitis appears as red, watery inflamed eyes. Common causes include:

- Allergies (to grass, pollen, house dust).
- Injury to the eye (cat scratch, after car accident, pricked by a bush).
- Foreign matter in the eye (grass seed, sand, etc).
- Sun irritation (especially in a white cat lacking a dark protective pigment around the eyes, or any cat with pink or pale eyelids).
- Chemical irritation (due to soap or shampoo or insecticide getting into the eye).
- Bacterial infection.
- Cat flu.

Other conditions of the eyelid, such as inturned eyelids, or inflammation of the skin around the eye (leading to the cat rubbing at the eye), can also result in conjuctivitis.

As a general rule, one watery eye suggests injury or a foreign body in the eye whereas two watery eyes suggests allergy or infection. Note that cat flu can start with one watery eye.

Rare causes of conjuctivitis are:

- Cancer.
- Parasite in the eye.
- Fungal infection.
- TB.

Treatment

Keep inflamed eye out of the sun. See your vet as soon as possible. Do not treat a blood-shot eye casually. Always seek veterinary advice. A watery eye can be the start of cat flu or be an indication of deeper problems within the eye. Do *not* use antibiotic eye ointment without veterinary advice.

Lift the nose up with one hand and rest the hand holding the eye ointment or drops against the cat's head. **Hold the nozzle well away from the eye** so that the eye is **not** touched even when the cat moves his head. Place one drop onto the eyeball and hold the lids apart with the nose up for a minute or two. A matchhead size of warm ointment is placed on the eyeball. For stiff ointments in cold weather, warm the naked end of the nozzle in warm water to make it flow more easily out of the tube

Sudden swelling

Sudden swelling of the eyelids (chemosis)can be due to allergic reactions, such as insect bites, hives, allergens in medications (e.g. neomycin); or it could be of unknown cause. A markedly swollen eye needs urgent veterinary attention.

Bacterial infection

Yellow or green pus discharging from the eye indicates bacterial infection. A scant, light grey discharge may be normal.

Flu viruses

Most infectious conjunctivitis is due to viral upper respiratory tract infection (sometimes called URTI). Anti-viral drugs are needed for the eyes. If pus comes from the eyes, antibiotic ointment is needed as well. Viral infection of the kitten's eyes can cause severe damage to the conjunctiva and cornea, causing the eyelids to stick to the eyeball.

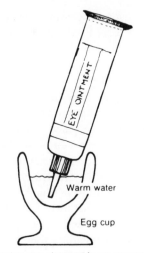

Warming eye ointment in an egg cup

FACIAL STAINING

Breeds with a white face can have a red-brown stain on the facial hair below the eye. This is due to tears overflowing from the eyelids and running down the face. This chronic wetness plus pigments in the tears turn the hair a rusty colour.

Every normal eye is constantly covered with a thin film of tears that keeps the eyeball lubricated, sweeps debris and bacteria from

the eye and prevents the cornea from drying out. In most cases, these tears are drained away by the tear ducts. Sometimes these tear ducts become blocked or are too narrow. Instead of being drained away into the nose, the tears spill over on to the face. In other cases, the tear flow may be excessive, overwhelm the capacity of the tear ducts and spill over. Such excessive tear flow can result from chronic irritation to the eyes, for example, from misdirected eyelashes, or eye rolled inward (discussed earlier in this chapter).

Staining is seen most often in Persians, but other cats can also be affected. The breed standard from Persians calls for large prominent eyes and a flat face. In consequence, the pooling space at the inner corner of the eye might be too small, or the tear duct might not be in the best location for effective drainage. Narrowing of the tear duct is another possibility.

Avoid breeding for a flat face. It can cause an overflow of tears with unsightly staining of the hair below the eyes.

Treatment
You can improve your cat's appearance by clipping the hair close to its face. Under veterinary supervision an antibiotic, tetracycline, is

given by mouth for 3 weeks. The tetracyline replaces that part of the tears which causes tears to stain fur. If the stain returns after treatment, then long-term administration might be considered. Unnecessary use of any antibiotic is, of course, highly undesirable.

DRY EYE

An eye without its covering of tears is called a dry eye (also called *keratoconjunctivitis sicca* or KCS). Dry eye is due to disease of the tear glands that produce the tears (not the tear duct, which drains the tears to the nose). No tears means no protection or lubrication to keep the eyeball healthy. A dry eye can be easily overlooked. It is a very irritating and potentially blinding disease.

A dry eye looks similar to other inflamed eyes except that pus sits on the surface of the eyeball rather than accumulating in the corners of the eye. If the tear flow is adequate, pus does not stick to the eyeball.

Home care
The dry eye needs to be kept constantly wet and clean. This can usually be achieved by applying artificial tears or a special formula supplied by your vet that stimulates tear production as well as lubricating the eyeball.

THE BLUE OR STEAMY EYE

The clear 'window' in the front of the eye through which light enters is called the cornea. If it is injured or irritated it could become inflamed and swell with fluid, changing from its normal clear transparency to a bluish colour. When inflamed the cornea appears cloudy or steamy.

Injury, allergy, infection, glaucoma and cancer can cause corneal damage. (*Note:* A cloudy eye is not a cataract. Cataracts are discussed later in this chapter.) A blue eye (cloudy cornea) indicates serious eye inflammation or increased pressure in the eyeball. Seek advice immediately.

EYE ULCERS

Signs
A red, sore, watery eye, which might be slightly blue. Half-closed eyelids could hide the ulcer, and the cat might wink one eye. A half-closed eye suggests a serious disease, such as a corneal ulcer or a foreign body.

Treatment

Ointments might be sufficient in very mild cases. Otherwise your vet might elect to stitch the third eyelid right across the eye. This 'bandages' the eye and is extremely useful in protecting the eye and accelerating healing. The vet might use a button to stop the stitches cutting into the skin of the upper lid. This looks peculiar but works very well.

GLAUCOMA

Glaucoma describes the result of many eye diseases in which there is an increase in pressure within the eyeball. The eyeball contains fluid (i.e. is aqueous), the amount of which is kept remarkably constant by a delicate, sensitive balance between production and drainage of fluid. Reduced drainage caused increased pressure, or glaucoma. Glaucoma can be very slow and insidious in its onset. Early cases are difficult to detect.

Reduced drainage at the indicated angle inside the eye leads to the eye becoming cloudy and causes considerable pain. The cat will typically not complain and becomes much brighter and happier following effective treatment

Increased pressure in the eye (glaucoma) is one of the causes of red eye, undetected headache and blue eye, and is usually seen in older cats. Cancer due, for example, to feline leukaemia or malignant melanoma, can cause glaucoma.

Diagnosis

Special instruments (tonometers) are necessary to detect early glaucoma, so diagnosis can be very difficult even for a vet. A specialist veterinary opthalmologist's examination might be required. The eye suffering from glaucoma is usually red and cloudy. The pupil is larger in size than the other eye and does not respond to a light shone on it. (The opening of the normal pupil should quickly contract when a bright penlight is shone through the pupil. Check one eye's reaction to light compared to the other eye.)

Treatment

Veterinary (often specialist) treatment can be very successful in controlling glaucoma, but glaucoma is usually not curable.

Treatment can include tropical or oral medication and surgery. If glaucoma is detected too late, blindness results and the eye becomes very large. Glaucoma is painful. The vet might recommend removal of the eye.

If the eye is painful, removal is the quickest way to relieve pain. Do not fear the look of an empty socket. When the hair regrows around the operation site, it will look most acceptable. Very few problems of after-care ever occur. If you want an artificial eye for your cat, discuss this before removal. Cats that have an eye removed usually manage extremely well, although they should not be allowed to roam as they are liable to be run over.

We are not always as aware of the pain of glaucoma as we should be. It is common for owners to say after surgery, 'I didn't realise the eye was worrying him so much—he is back to his old bright self now the eye has been removed.' In some cases, however, the cat does not appear to be worried by the blinded eye.

Q   *Will a large eyeball cause problems?*

If the vet tells you the pressure in the eye is low (pressure is best measured by a tonometer), the eye can be left as it is. Plastic surgery to make the eyelid smaller will protect the eyeball and prevent disease from exposure and drying. If the pressure within the eye is high, it is usually better to remove the eye. Alternatively, an artificial implant can be placed in the eyeball to make the eye comfortable and pleasing in appearance.

CATARACTS

A cataract is a cloudy lens. It is seen as a hazy eye or white pupil. Light cannot get through the affected lens to reach the back of the eye. A cataract is seen as opacity within the eyeball. This is easily confused with corneal disease, which is on the surface of the eye.

Causes

Any disturbance to the eye that upsets the delicate lens chemistry can cause the lens to become cloudy. The usual cause is inflammation inside the eyeball sometimes following injury to the eye. A disease in the body (e.g. diabetes), inflammation or disease in the eye,

When the lens becomes cloudy vision is decreased. See your vet as soon as any cloudy part is seen. Cataracts can be removed surgically and (unlike in people) no artifical lens needs to be placed in the eye after surgery

a blow to the head or old age can all lead to cataracts. If the cat contracts a disease during pregnancy, cataracts can even form in kittens while they are in her womb.

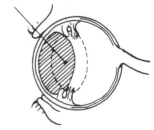

Lens dislocated forward

In older cats the lens in the eye can work loose, fall forward against the cornea and make the eye blue. To avoid pain, the lens is removed or relocated towards the retina

Treatment

Cataracts are not curable. In some cases eye drops that enlarge the pupil can allow some vision past a cloudy lens, but the change within the lens remains. Occasionally spontaneous partial disappearance or resorption of cataracts occurs in cats under three years of age.

An immediate examination by an eye specialist before the lens becomes too cloudy will determine whether the back of the eye (beyond the cloudy lens) is healthy. It is vital to learn whether the retina is healthy should surgical removal of the lens be considered later on. There is no point in removing a diseased lens if the back of the eye is also diseased.

In most cataracts, surgical extraction is not indicated. Moreover, medical treatment might be needed for other diseases in the eye. Many cats manage very well in spite of dense cataracts.

Cataract surgery

Surgery involves removing the affected lens to allow light to get to the sight receptors at the back of the eye. Surgery might be considered if there is no disease beyond the cataract or elsewhere in the eye. Results of surgery in the cat are generally good.

Q *Why does my cat's eye shine green at night?*

Reflection from a light such as headlights or a torch is due to the presence of a fluorescent reflective layer (the tapetum) at the back of the eyeball. In some cases, the reflection is red instead of green. This is sometimes called 'ruby eye', and it means that these cats lack this reflecting layer. The Siamese

Eyeshine is due to reflection through a large pupil from a layer at the back of the eye, which people do not possess. This layer helps the cat to see so well at night

cat might possess a chocolate-coloured tapetum rather than a greenish one, or the tapetum could be absent altogether, which might mean that these cats don't see as well at dusk and after dark as normal as cats with the reflecting layer.

Q *Can bright sunlight cause eye damage?*

The main danger of sunlight is to white cats or other cats with pink, unpigmented skin around the eyelids. Strong sunlight can cause sunburn and inflamed lids (and can lead to cancer). In cats already suffering from an eye disease, sunlight can make eye inflammation worse, so if your cat has a sick or sore eye keep it out of the sun.

Q *What are signs of eye pain? Is pain evident if a cat has a sore eye?*

Winking, squinting of the eye, holding the eye half closed and avoiding light can all indicate eye pain. In severe cases of eye disease the cat may not eat, becomes lethargic or irritable. A sore eye often causes no obvious pain. The cat suffers and we don't realise it. After the eye is cured owners will often remark on how the cat is back to its old self.

Q *What 'sleep' and eye discharge is normal, and what is not?*

Tiny glands at the front of the eye constantly produce a film of tears to keep the eye moist and lubricated. Residues of these tears or 'sleep' can accumulate in the corner of the eyes and then dry out. This is usually a light grey colour. Green, yellow, or watery or pink/brown discharge is not normal. Copious amounts of discharge are not normal.

Q *My kitten seems well but has had a runny eye ever since we got it. What do I do?*

Cat flu is a common cause of scarring of the tear ducts and faulty tear drainage. If it worries the cat, surgery might be indicated. An artificial tear duct can be inserted in the eye. This delicate surgery should preferably be done by a specialist with an operating microscope. If the cat is not worried by it we usually leave it alone.

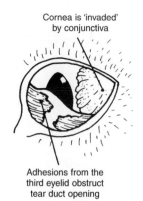

Cornea is 'invaded' by conjunctiva

Adhesions from the third eyelid obstruct tear duct opening

Q *My old cat has a blue lens. Is this a cataract?*

Usually not. The blue lens you see in most old cats is not from disease, but due to the hardening of the lens with age.

Q *My old cat's eye suddenly looks more blue and cloudy. Should I see the vet?*

Yes. Sudden changes often reflect painful conditions. For example, its lens might have suddenly fallen forward against the cornea. This not only affects vision but also can be painful. In addition, we need to check that the lens of the other eye is not loose and about to dislocate. You might be referred to a specialist for this examination.

13 SKIN AND COAT

GROOMING YOUR CAT

Daily grooming of longhaired cats is essential to prevent knotting and matting. For shorthaired cats a brush and comb twice weekly is adequate. Old cats or sick cats might lose interest in grooming themselves. Regular grooming by you under these circumstances is usually appreciated by your cat and will help maintain a healthy coat.

Coat care should be started when the kitten is about three months old. The cat then becomes accustomed to the activity. Most cats enjoy brushing provided you are gentle but firm. A cat that hasn't been brushed before will probably be a little wary at first. Introduce the brush gradually. A little brushing at a time. The cat will soon see that there is nothing to be frightened of. It would help if the cat associates grooming with a reward, such as a fishy treat.

Grooming equipment

A natural bristle brush is best. Synthetic bristles can cause hair damage, especially in longhaired cats. To remove dead hairs, comb against the lie of the hair with a metal comb.

Bathing

A bath might become necessary if the cat gets very muddy or soiled by diarrhoea, oil or other tenacious material. A badly soiled cat could be reluctant to lick itself clean because of the offensive taste. Ingestion of some materials such as sump oil is potentially dangerous. These toxic materials must be removed by bathing.

When bathing the cat, use a shampoo specifically formulated for cats. If one is not available, then a mild baby shampoo or a mild pure soap will do. These are less likely to irritate the eyes or skin than perfumed soaps or strong shampoos. Detergents manufactured for dish or clothes washing are unsuitable—*do not* use them on your cat. Always thoroughly rinse any soap or shampoo from the coat afterwards.

Matting

Matting can be a serious problem in longhaired cats. Try to prevent it. Daily grooming will ensure that tangles don't turn into immovable wads of hair. Matting starts in areas that are difficult for the cat to groom. The most commonly affected areas are between the shoulders, behind the ears, under the chin, under the arms and legs and beneath the tail. Matts under the arms and on the chest can become a problem as some cats resent having these areas brushed. By dividing a large matt into smaller matts and combing these clumps you will be able to tease apart some of the tangled hair. In other cases it will be necessary to cut the clumps of hair out. Use blunt-ended scissors and take special care not to nick the skin. Whatever you do, do *not* wet the coat when trying to remove a matt—it will make it worse.

Matts should always be removed before bathing.

In longhaired cats that either won't tolerate brushing or that have been neglected, electric clippers might be needed to shear off the matted hair. In extreme cases a general anaesthetic could even be necessary.

Fur balls/hairballs

Hair is continually shed from the cat's coat. The tongue of the cat acts as a comb and helps remove these loose hairs. The barbs on the cat's tongue trap the hairs, and they are swallowed. During periods of heavy moulting (spring and summer) particularly in longhaired breeds, hair will accumulate in solid masses in the stomach. These are called hairballs and are eliminated either by vomiting (which is a normal and natural occurrence and not a cause for concern), or they might pass into the intestines to be expelled in the droppings. If a hairball is very large, constipation could occur. Regular dosing with paraffin oil (dose: ½ teaspoon twice weekly) during the moulting period helps to clear hair from the bowel. Mix the paraffin with food or syringe it straight into the mouth.

Cats irritated by hair trapped at the back of their throats will cough.

Hairs could become entwined around the teeth and irritate the gums. As a result, the cat will paw at the mouth and drool, and there might be a foul mouth odour. You should be able to remove these hairs fairly easily. A general anaesthetic is sometimes needed in an obstinate cat.

If you remove the dead hairs by daily grooming most of these problems can be avoided.

Removal of substances from cat's coat

Paint
Allow the paint to harden, then cut off the paint and hair. *Never* use thinners or solvents on or near the cat's skin as they can cause severe chemical burning of the skin.

Crude (e.g. sump) oil

Wash the cat in vegetable oil or margarine several times. Both of these products combine chemically with sump oil and allow it to be removed more efficiently. When most of the oil is removed, wash the cat with warm, soapy water (use a mild toilet soap). Rinse thoroughly. Repeat until all traces of oil are eliminated.

Skunk oil

Soak the oily area in tomato juice.
Thoroughly bath in warm soapy water (use a mild toilet soap). A dilute solution of ammonia can be used if the first two steps are not effective. Rinse thoroughly after using the dilute ammonia solution.

NAILS

Nails grow continuously so cats must keep their nails trimmed and sharpened. They do this by actively clawing at objects such as the base of trees and posts. You could provide a scratching post if you like. Natural wearing down also occurs during daily activities such as climbing. Cats that don't exercise because they are housebound, elderly or sick can grow excessively long nails. These cats need regular nail trimming, particularly on the front paws. Trimming a cat's nails is a simple, painless procedure if the cat cooperates.

Before the nails are clipped, identify the pink part (the 'quick'). Avoid cutting into the quick as it contains nerves and blood vessels.

If a nail does start to bleed exert pressure over it with a cotton-ball for 5 minutes if you can, although most cats resent this attention. Otherwise, don't worry as the bleeding will soon stop spontaneously. The cat will not lose much blood.

Nail bed infection

Infections can occur in the nailfold. These infections are difficult to treat successfully and could become chronic.

Treatment

Mild cases respond to antiseptic soaks or painting with iodine. In severe cases, or in some cases that are not responding to treat-

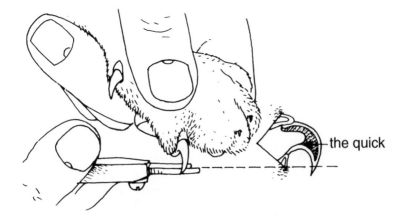

the quick

ment, the nail needs to be removed. This allows the infected area to drain. Infection might involve bacteria, yeast or fungi. The choice of drug treatment will vary accordingly. Your vet will advise you on the most appropriate treatment for your cat. In most cases the nail will grow back normally after the infection has been cured.

FLEAS

Fleas are the most common cause of skin disease in cats. Most cats get fleas sooner or later, so all cat owners should read this section.

The flea's lifecycle occurs both on and off the host. A single cat can support as many as 15 000 fleas. Each female flea lays about 200–400 eggs in her lifetime, so large numbers of fleas can build up quickly. Flea eggs are pinpoint-sized, white and oval in shape. They are very hard to see with the naked eye. They are resistant to many insecticides.

Fleas can cause four problems:

1 Transmit disease and parasites (especially tapeworm).
2 Cause skin irritation and itching, leading to vigorous scratching and licking, which in turn damages the skin. This can preoccupy some cats to such an extent that their appetite wanes and they lose weight.
3 Fleas suck blood, which can cause anaemia if they are present in large numbers.
4 After prolonged exposure to biting fleas some cats develop a sensitivity (allergy) to flea saliva, which can result in a severe skin condition termed flea allergy dermatitis (discussed below). Once sensitised, even a single flea bite could trigger an acute itch.

Signs

Fleas spend some of their life off the cat. Not seeing any does not necessarily mean that they are not present. Look instead for indications that they have been around. Fleas leave evidence of their presence as flea dirt, which is actually flea excreta and consists mainly of digested blood. These droppings appear as small black specks within the coat. They are most readily seen by pushing the hair back against its natural lie. Flea dirt is present in the highest concentrations around the tail base and neck.

If you are not convinced that the matter you find there is flea dirt, brush some of the specks on to a piece of white paper. Add a few drops of water to the specks and within a few seconds the water turns reddish brown due to the blood pigments in the excreta. This is evidence that what you are seeing is digested blood and not just dirt.

Flea control

In order to control fleas it is not enough to kill them. You must also deal with the eggs that have already been laid, ready to hatch into a new crop. In an average house, where the cat has been infested for a few months, there will be millions of eggs, which cannot be vacuumed up and are resistant to most chemical treatments. The most successful long-term programs break the lifecycle of the flea. This is a far better approach than simply saturating the cat or its home with insecticides.

Break the breeding cycle

Each flea can lay between 200 and 400 eggs in their lifetime. The eggs hatch to larvae, which live on debris in cracks, at the base of your carpet or in the cat's bedding. The larvae turn into pupae, protected by a cocoon, and they sit waiting for weeks to months before emerging as adult fleas. For every flea on your cat there are likely to be 20 eggs, pupae and larvae waiting to take their place.

A range of products that prevent fleas from laying eggs is now available. They contain ingredients such as lufenuron. Given once a month with the cat's food, any flea feeding from the cat will not lay any more eggs. Ultimately all the eggs, larvae and pupae already present in your environment will develop into adults, but they will not be replaced and so the flea population will dwindle to zero. This might take a few months, and therefore you might have to use something to kill the adult fleas during that period. These egg control programs are excellent, but they can be expensive, especially if you have lots of cats and/or dogs, because you must treat all your animals if you are to achieve success.

Insecticides

With all forms of insecticides, for maximum effectiveness and safety it is important to read and follow the manufacturer's directions. Do not use any product that does not specifically say it is safe to use on cats.

Area foggers

Area foggers (or flea 'bombs') contain ingredients that prevent the flea eggs from developing into adult fleas. These are called insect growth regulators (IGRs). They enjoy a large margin of safety and last up to nine months. In situations such as apartments or small houses they can be very successful. Follow the manufacturer's instructions exactly for best results.

Flea powders

Many effective flea powders are available, but few last more than a few days and therefore, to keep the cat flea-free, they must be reapplied about twice a week. This varies, so read the directions. After dusting the cat, be certain to work the powder deep down on to the skin and then to remove any excess from the surface of the coat by wiping it with a damp towel or something similar. Otherwise, the cat will ingest the powder while grooming and might become ill.

Sprays

Sprays can be effective. However, most cats resent being sprayed, and it is more difficult to remove excess insecticide from the surface of the coat than with powder.

Collars

Flea collars contain one of a range of insecticides. Some are released as vapours, others as tiny particles that work their way through the cat's coat. Some cats seem to respond well to these insecticidal collars, but for others they are not completely effective. Collars that contain IGRs, which prevent the hatching of flea eggs, are also available.

Oral insecticides

Some insecticides, such as cythioate, are given orally. Fleas subsequently feeding from the treated cat will pick up a lethal dose of the insecticide. Most of these products need to be given every few days to maintain effective levels. Their safety level is good, and the insecticide does not contaminate the environment.

Spot on preparations

Some safe spot on preparations are now available. They spread over the cat's skin without being absorbed. They last about a month.

Treatment of young kittens

Kittens suckling from a queen that has fleas often have fleas too. If the flea burden is high, severe blood loss and even death could occur in the kittens. It is essential to eliminate fleas on the queen. Either a flea powder or rinse can be used. Take special care to wash the nipples clean after using any insecticidal preparation as young kittens are very susceptible to these poisons.

FLEAS !!!

Kittens themselves may be dipped in lukewarm water for 2–3 minutes to drown any fleas on them. Make sure the fur on the head is saturated by dabbing it with a wet sponge. Dry them thoroughly using a towel and then a hair dryer or fan heater. Beware of overheating the kitten. Fresh clean bedding should be provided and the old bedding burnt.

Flea allergy dermatitis

Some cats develop an allergy to flea saliva. These cats become extremely sensitive to any flea bite. A single bite can result in severe skin irritation called flea allergy dermatitis or miliary dermatitis. By scratching and licking themselves the skin is further damaged. The sensory nerves of the skin become inflamed and exposed, creating an even more intense desire to scratch. This leads to a vicious cycle: itch, scratch, itch, scratch. Sores develop. They are felt in the skin as numerous small crusty lesions. They have characteristic distribution.

Treatment

If the condition is severe, it will be necessary for a vet to relieve the irritation with a dose of cortisone or a similar drug to allow the damaged skin time to heal. During this period start a vigorous campaign to eliminate fleas on the cat and in the immediate environment.

Stick fast flea

The stick fast poultry flea (*Echidnophagia gallinacea*) prefers birds but can infest cats. They usually feed around the head and ears of the cat, and resemble mud stuck to the skin and hair. These fleas do not move about when disturbed but hang tenaciously to the skin. They are controlled by the same methods outlined for general flea management.

LICE

Lice rarely occur in healthy, well-cared-for cats. They are usually seen only on neglected, run down or sick cats. Cats suffering from disease will become listless and cease grooming.

Lice can then take advantage of the cat's disinterest and parasitise it. Cat lice don't like other animals, so an infested cat is not a risk to humans or other pets. There are two types of lice: biting lice, which cause skin irritation, and other types, which suck blood and cause anaemia.

Signs

Lice can be found anywhere on the body. The skin becomes itchy, and the hair matts or falls out. There may be self-inflicted sores where the cat has licked the itchy skin. The tiny white lice can be found by looking under the matts. Lice eggs ('nits') are attached to the hair shafts and give the appearance of scattered flour on the cat's coat.

Treatment

Matts of hair should be removed by clipping. The cat should have an insecticidal rinse once weekly for one month. *Or* wash the cat in an insecticidal shampoo and then apply an insecticidal preparation. This should be repeated weekly for a month. If the skin is extensively damaged, veterinary advice should be sought before the cat is treated with any insecticidal preparation. The problem that caused the initial self-neglect should also be remedied.

MANGE

For centuries the word *mange* has been used to describe a multitude of skin conditions. A 'mangy' cat was understood to be poorly kept or rundown. In fact mange is a specific skin condition caused by mites that infest the skin. In cats the most significant cause of mange is a particular mite called *notoedres cati*. Mange is no longer a common condition. Insecticides now available are very effective. When mange does occur it is usually seen in cats that are not robust, such as the very old cat, or in a litter of poorly nourished young kittens.

Mange is highly contagious between cats.

A mange mite

Signs

The mites burrow deeply into the skin, causing intense itching and irritation. The cat continuously rubs, scratches or licks the affected areas. Mange usually starts on the edge of the ears and then progresses to cover the face, eyelids and neck. The feet could be affected if mites are transferred from the head to the feet during grooming. In the same way mites could be transferred to the tail base and hind legs. The whole body might eventually become affected.

Other signs include self-inflicted sores, hair loss, areas of thickening and wrinkling of the skin. Bacteria can invade the broken skin and cause serious infections.

Treatment

When the condition is extensive, veterinary attention is necessary. Treatment could include antibiotics, insecticides and perhaps drugs to relieve the itch.

In mild cases a 0.5% malathion rinse repeated once (in 10 days) will kill the mites and allow the skin to heal. All cats in contact with the infected cat should also be treated with malathion. The mite can survive only a short time off the cat, so bedding and grooming equipment are not a source of reinfection.

Prevention

Regular treatment with insecticidal preparations such as are used for flea control will effectively control mites.

Q *Are people affected by cat mites?*

The cat mite can survive for only a short time on people. During this time minor skin irritation may occur. It is only on the skin of cats, rabbits or foxes that it can take up permanent residence and cause extensive skin damage.

FLY STRIKE

Fly strike occurs when blow-flies lay eggs in matted hair, especially around the tail or open wounds. After the eggs hatch the maggots burrow into the skin, producing extensive skin damage. They also carry bacterial infection into wounds.

Treatment

The matted hair and hairs surrounding damaged skin should be trimmed away. Use a mild antiseptic such as dilute hydrogen peroxide to flush the wound. Remove as many maggots as possible and then apply an insecticidal, antiseptic powder or cream to kill any remaining maggots and to prevent reinfestation.

In some cases veterinary attention will be necessary, especially if the area involved is extensive and the cat resents attention to it.

Prevention

Don't let matts of hair build up. Aged or debilitated cats will be unable to groom themselves properly, and it is your responsibility to keep them free of matts. Don't let loose droppings accumulate in hair around the hind legs. Longhaired cats with diarrhoea will inevitably form some matts soiled with faeces, which must be trimmed away. The area around the tail base should be examined routinely for matts.

BOT FLIES

Found in some parts of the USA and Europe, bot flies (*habronema* spp. *draschia* spp) produce a different form of fly strike. The maggots migrate through the skin and are seen as swellings along the neck, back, sides, belly, eyelids, nostrils or jaw. The grub breathes through an opening at the top of this swelling. These lumps could become infected and full of pus, especially if the grub dies.

Treatment

First, remove the grub by squeezing the lump or gently pulling it out using tweezers. Then flush the lump with antiseptic solution. In cases where there are multiple swellings, veterinary treatment will be needed.

RINGWORM

Ringworm is an unfortunate name as this skin condition is not caused by a worm at all. It is caused by a fungus. Originally it was believed that the characteristic round ringworm sores were caused by a worm burrowing around in circles under the skin. In fact, the reason ringworm sores are round is because, like the ripples produced when a pebble is thrown into a pond, the fungus starts in one spot and spreads in all directions simultaneously.

The incidence of ringworm is highest in hot, humid climates such as the southern USA and most of South America, northern Australia, Spain and North Africa, but is seen in most parts of the world.

Signs

Symptoms appear 2–4 weeks after infection and vary greatly in appearance. A mild infection might have produced only a few

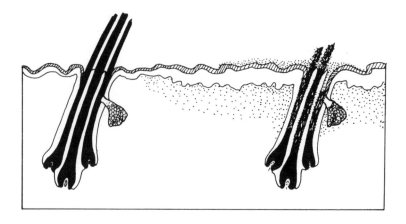

Ringworm: The fungus attacks the skin and the hairs. Infections run deep into the hair follicle

broken hairs on the face or ears. There could be small round or oval patches of hair loss on the head, ears, forepaws or back. In some cases the lesion could be mistaken for food stuck on the end of the cat's nose or face. In severe cases there are large areas of hair loss with crusty scaly scabs. Occasionally ringworm fungus will cause infection around the toenails.

Unlike ringworm in people, the sores are not particularly itchy. There will be mild irritation, but generally the cat pays little attention to them, and general health is unaffected.

Young cats are more susceptible to ringworm than older cats. Following infection a strong immunity to reinfection develops.

Diagnosis
If you suspect your cat has ringworm you should consult your vet. He or she will shine an ultraviolet light (called a Wood's lamp) on the suspicious area and this causes some ringworm to fluoresce. A sample of the affected hair and skin might be sent to a laboratory for examination. Sometimes the vet will be confident enough of the characteristic appearance of the ringworm lesion and will treat accordingly without obtaining laboratory confirmation.

Treatment
Many mild cases are self-limiting and will clear up without treatment. Because ringworm is transmissible to humans (children are

particularly susceptible) treatment might be advisable. If there are only one or two ringworm sores the area can be painted with tincture of iodine or washed with antiseptic soap to kill the fungal spores. The hairs around the area should be clipped, but you must disinfect the scissors afterwards and burn the clippings. If there are many sores it would be more effective to shampoo with a fungicidal product, e.g. hexetidine.

TRANSMITTED

TO HUMANS

Rinsing in 1:200 dilution of 45% captan is also effective. Either treatment should be repeated twice weekly until the sores resolve.

In severe or persistent cases, an anti-fungal drug called griseofulvin may be given orally for 3–6 weeks. It is highly effective, but is available only by prescription and should be used under veterinary supervision.

It is advisable either to burn or disinfect bedding and to disinfect grooming equipment. Fungal spores can remain infective for 6 months if not destroyed.

Disinfectants such as iodophos, formalin and alcohol are effective against fungal spores but are too toxic to be used on the cat itself.

Q   *Is ringworm contagious between cats?*

Yes, but older cats often have a good immunity to ringworm and usually don't develop lesions. If your cat has been in contact with a cat with ringworm, griseofulvin can be given to prevent ringworm developing. You should discuss this with your vet as griseofulvin can only be given under veterinary supervision.

Some cats carry the fungal spores around in their coat without showing signs of having ringworm. These cats can act as sources of infection for other animals (and people). Because of these 'carriers', once ringworm gets into a cattery it is very difficult to eliminate.

Q   *Can people catch ringworm from cats?*

Yes, but ringworm can also be picked up from many other sources, including other people and dogs, or even directly from the soil. Children are especially susceptible, but adults can be infected too. Ringworm is not a particularly severe condition in humans and usually responds quickly to ointments and lotions. In some cases it becomes deep-seated or spreads rapidly. Don't take chances; see your physician for advice.

HORMONAL SKIN DISEASE

Feline endocrine alopecia

Hair loss (alopecia) is sometimes seen in neutered cats. It is much more common in castrated males than in spayed females.

Signs

There is no itchiness or change in the appearance of the skin. The only sign is a thinning of the hair coat in a symmetrical pattern. There is never a total loss of all body hair. A few fine hairs might remain on affected areas. The cat shows no other signs of illness.

Treatment

This condition is sometimes difficult to treat successfully. Some cats respond to hormone treatment. Finding the actual cure for the condition is often a matter of trial and error. Treatment is continued until the hair regrows. In some cases the condition does not recur; in others a low dose of hormone will be needed intermittently for life. This is a matter for you and your vet to discuss.

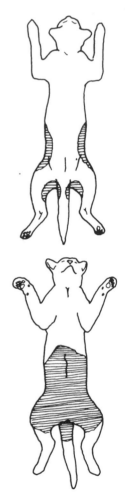

The pattern of hair loss in feline endocrine alopecia

Feline acne

Cats sometimes develop blackheads (comedomes) or pimples (pustules) on the face, mainly around the lip margins or under the chin. These can be quite severe, producing small abscesses that are difficult to cure.

Cats that don't wash and groom themselves properly under their chins and around their faces are prone to this condition. Dirt accumulates and blocks the pores. Oily secretions then accumulate, and blackheads form. They may become infected, producing pimples and small abscesses.

Treatment

First thoroughly clean the neglected areas with mild antiseptic
soap or antiseptic skin solutions,
then swab the area with alcohol or
methylated spirits. In some cases,
antibiotics will be necessary to clear
up the infection.

Feline acne

Prevention

Cats prone to acne need their
chins cleaned routinely for them.
Alternate between an antiseptic agent, such as hexachlorophene,
and a defatting agent, such as alcohol or methylated spirits. It is
usually only necessary to treat these cats twice a week to prevent
a flare up.

Stud tail

Stud tail is a common condition in uncastrated males. The male
cat, under the influence of the male sex hormone testosterone, produces an oily secretion from glands at the base of the tail. It can
result in an unsightly, greasy patch of hair in the gland area, which
is particularly noticeable in light-coloured cats. It usually does not
concern the cat unless the area becomes irri-
tated or infected.

Treatment

Wash the area with a cat shampoo, a baby shampoo or mild toilet soap to degrease the area and
eliminate the stain. This treatment should be
repeated daily, especially in the breeding section
(spring). If infection occurs your vet might
advise the use of antibiotics. Castration is the
only effective way of eliminating the problem
permanently.

Stud tail

HYPERTHYROID

Hyperthyroid is almost exclusively a disease of
older cats, but it is now considered to be the
most common endocrine disease of cats (i.e.
disease caused by hormone upsets). It wasn't known to be a

problem until about 1979, so it has been recognised as a disease relatively recently.

The thyroid is actually a pair of glands situated at the base of the cat's neck. In humans and dogs the most common problem associated with the thyroid is *under*-production of the thyroid hormones (termed '*hypo*thyroidism'). In cats, it is usually the reverse. There is excess production of these hormones, or *hyper*thyroidism. The cause of hyperthyroidism is usually a tumour of one or both thyroid glands.

The major signs are listed below. Not all may be present.

*   Weight loss.
*   Increased appetite.
*   Increased activity, even hyperactivity.
*   Irritability.
*   Coat might become poor—dry and scaly or 'tatty'.
*   Diarrhoea—often very 'fatty' or greasy.
*   Increased thirst.
*   Increased heart rate (sometimes more than 240 beats a minute).

Occasionally hyperthyroid cats are seen with none of these signs. Instead they are weak, depressed or apathetic and will not eat. Their muscles are weak so the head hangs down.

Diagnosis

Hyperthyroidism is diagnosed via blood tests, which measure the level of thyroid hormones in the blood.

Treatment

Many cats respond extremely well to medical management, with oral drugs such as carbamizole, although surgical removal of the tumour might be necessary. Radioactive iodine is another treatment that usually gives excellent results, but it is not always available and can be expensive.

Other treatment might also be needed, for example to reduce the heart rate and for complications arising from poor heart function.

FELINE MILIARY DERMATITIS

Some cases of feline miliary dermatitis (FMD) are caused by flea bite allergy (see 'Fleas' earlier in this chapter). Other causes include food allergy, parasitic diseases, and several other factors.

Signs

*   Multiple, small, scabby sores across the rump, lower back and neck areas. These scabs are not always visible, but they can be felt by stroking the cat.

- Thinning of the hair coat in the affected areas (also makes sores more obvious).
- Thickening of the skin.
- Scratching, licking and biting at the sores causing more skin damage and hair loss.

Treatment

Veterinary treatment could include the use of steroids, vitamin supplements, dietary changes or hormone replacement. Treatment is usually very successful but in some cases will have to be maintained at a low level for life.

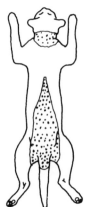

LICK SORES

If a cat persistently licks an area of skin, the rasp-like action of the tongue will eventually damage the skin and produce a sore, called lick sores (or *acral lick dermatitis*).

Licking is a normal part of grooming, but some cats concentrate their attention on one particular area, and a problem begins. Stress is the main cause of overgrooming, although some lick sores start as a wound, graze or insect bite. Highly strung, nervous cats are the most likely to develop lick sores. Licking can start as a casual habit. Some cats achieve a tension release by grooming themselves in much the same way a child relieves anxiety by sucking its thumb. Constant licking, however, irritates the nerves in the skin, and an itch develops.

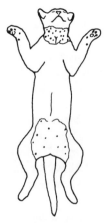

These areas are affected in cases of miliary dermatitis

The cat then licks more, partly to relieve the itch—and the skin becomes further damaged. Continuous licking prevents healing and eventually can create deep ulcers.

Signs

At first, hair loss is noticed where the cat is persistently licking. If licking persists the area becomes red and inflamed, the skin breaks and an ulcer forms.

Treatment

A lick sore can be difficult to clear up. Treatment should commence as early as possible. If the skin is hairless and red, providing

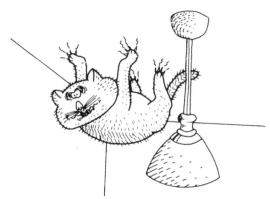

Nervous cats seem to be particularly prone to skin disease, especially lick sores

the cat with distracting toys or a companion will relieve boredom and prevent the problem advancing further. If the skin is ulcerated or the cat cannot be distracted, veterinary treatment is required.

A vet will often use cortisone to relieve the skin irritation as this reduces the cat's desire to lick, allowing the skin to heal. In neurotic cats, hormonal treatment might be successful. In refractory cases surgical removal of the sore could be considered.

Prevention

Where boredom is the cause, you could try some of the following:
- Provide more 'people' attention.
- Allow the cat a window to look out of.
- More feline company—a new cat. But *beware*—this can backfire and even make the problem worse.
- Avoid close confinement for long periods.
- Give toys to divert the cat's attention.
- Leave a radio playing when you leave the house.
- Try to minimise any suspected sources of anxiety.
  Read chapter 5 on 'Behaviour'.

FOOD ALLERGY DERMATITIS

Although food allergies occur in cats, they are not common. Such allergies can occur at any time of the cat's life with or without a sudden dietary change.

Signs

Signs are a generalised itchiness with reddening of the skin, weals (hives) or small scabby sores (miliary dermatitis), and sometimes vomiting and/or diarrhoea.

Treatment

An elimination diet is the best way to identify the offending food. The cat is placed on a bland diet containing few ingredients with no preservatives or additives. The idea is to feed a protein source that is not normally part of the cat's diet. Choose from fish, chicken, minced beef, lamb or mutton and feed it for 10–14 days. If food allergy is the problem, there should be a remission of the skin lesions within this time. If the change in diet seems to have succeeded, try feeding a small amount of the suspected food again (e.g. canned or dry food it normally eats). If signs of the allergy reappear within 12–24 hours the offending food is identified. If this food is not the cause (i.e. the signs do not reappear) continue returning other components of the diet on alternate days until the one causing the allergy is eventually identified.

14 THE GUT

REGURGITATION AND VOMITING

Regurgitation

Regurgitation of food might seem to be the same as vomiting, but there are differences. Regurgitation is a relatively passive emptying of the stomach and usually results from overeating. The food is brought up fairly sluggishly, in contrast to the more dramatic, forceful act of vomiting.

If your cat frequently regurgitates food, try feeding more often, but much smaller quantities. Regurgitation could be due to a blockage or obstruction, so consult your vet if your cat regurgitates food after eating if this is out of character.

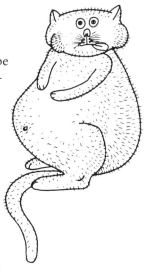

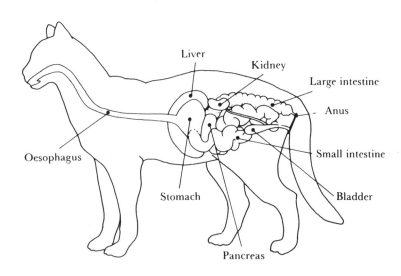

Vomiting

Vomiting is a natural reflex, designed to clear the stomach of potentially irritant or toxic matter. Vomiting is also a part of many disease states. It does not necessarily indicate that the stomach itself is the seat of the problem.

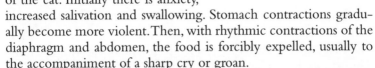

Vomiting can be differentiated from regurgitation by the behaviour of the cat. Initially there is anxiety, increased salivation and swallowing. Stomach contractions gradually become more violent. Then, with rhythmic contractions of the diaphragm and abdomen, the food is forcibly expelled, usually to the accompaniment of a sharp cry or groan.

Vomiting can be a useful function that eliminates substances that could otherwise cause further problems. It might also be a sign of serious disease.

When to call the vet

If the cat is vomiting *and:*
- The cat is listless or physically depressed.
- There is profuse diarrhoea.
- There is blood in the vomit.
- Vomit is 'faecal' in nature, that is, more like bowel motion than stomach contents.
- Vomiting is persistent.

Minor causes of vomiting

Grass eating

Sometimes cats will eat specific types of grass to induce vomiting. This is generally just to clear the stomach, perhaps because it is overfull or partly blocked by some indigestible matter, such as a hairball or feathers from a bird. Once the cat has vomited, the condition is usually resolved. If the grass eating is abnormally frequent, consult your vet.

Travel or motion sickness

For highly strung or emotional cats your vet could supply you with a mild sedative before a long trip. Do not use human travel sickness preparations unless on the advice of your vet. Most cats travel without vomiting, although they might yowl constantly.

Constipation

Toxins are absorbed from the bowel of the constipated cat, making it nauseous. Vomiting might result.

Worms

A heavy burden of roundworm can prevent the normal passage of food. Sometimes roundworm irritate the stomach itself, although they usually live in the small intestine. Treat as for worms (discussed later in this chapter).

Gulping

Some cats rush their food, gulping it down and failing to chew it at all. These cats can ingest quite a large volume of air with the food. The stomach becomes over-disintended, triggering a reflex-clearing vomit.

Cut the food finer, and feed smaller amounts more often. You might have to give four or five small meals a day. Feeding a less appetising food, such as dry food, might also work.

Sensitivity to a particular food

You might note that your cat is vomiting whenever it eats a particular type or brand of food. This could be a reaction to the food itself or to a preservative or additive in the food. Change the cat's diet to a bland food that is unlikely to cause problems, such as chicken or mutton. When the cat has returned to normal, offer a little of the suspect food. If vomiting is repeated, your suspicions will be confirmed.

If the cat is reacting to one of the preservatives or additives in commercially manufactured foods you might have to experiment a little before you discover a range of foods that your cat can cope with.

Stress

Some emotional or highly strung cats vomit when excited or upset, such as when the cat is fed alongside other cats. Nervous cats are usually better fed separately (not just a couple of metres from the other cats but in a separate room). Allow the cat a few days to adjust to this new routine. Other stresses can similarly result in vomiting. It can be difficult to discover what is upsetting the cat. Read chapter 5 on 'Behaviour' for some ideas.

Serious vomiting

The types of vomiting discussed below are more serious than those discussed above, and should be investigated.

Vomiting blood

The blood could come from the mouth, oesophagus or stomach. When a cat vomits blood after a car accident, it does not necessarily indicate serious internal damage. Quite often, the blood has come from a cut tongue or a knocked-out tooth.

Possible causes of bleeding in the oesophagus or stomach include laceration by foreign bodies such as bone splinters, fish hooks or needles, or bleeding from ulcers or tumours.

Projectile vomiting

In projectile vomiting, the stomach contents are ejected forcibly and without much warning to land up to 30 cm away from the cat. Projectile vomiting usually indicates a blockage at the start or early part of the duodenum. The most common site is the 'exit valve' from the stomach (the pyloric sphincter). This is a muscular ring that normally seals the stomach, opening only to let regulated amounts of food out of the stomach and into the small intestine.

Blockages could be caused by hairballs, growths or foreign bodies such as bits of plastic or rubber.

In some kittens, projectile vomiting starts when they are given solid foods. In such cases, the cause is often a constriction or 'stricture' of the pyloric sphincter. The kitten can open the sphincter enough to let liquids through, but solids cannot pass.

Treatment is surgical. Usually it is successful, and the kitten can develop without further complications.

GASTRITIS

Gastritis means 'inflamed stomach'. The primary sign of gastritis is vomiting. Some of the causes of gastritis include:
- Eating spoiled foods.
- Eating foods contaminated with insecticides or herbicides (neither are particularly common as the cat is very careful about what it eats.
- Ingesting irritant substances while grooming. The cat's fur could become contaminated with materials such as sump oil, or

the owner might dust the coat with insecticide but neglect to remove the superficial powder. In these or similar situations, the cat's fastidious grooming habits could result in the ingestion of toxic amounts of these substances.

- Ulcers. Stomach ulcers are rare in cats. They sometimes occur as part of other conditions, such as advanced kidney disease.

Home treatment

Home treatment should only be contemplated if the cat is still bright and alert, the vomit is free of blood, and there is not an accompanying diarrhoea. If the vomiting persists despite home treatment, consult your vet.

- 'Rest' the stomach. Give *no* food for at least 12 hours. In mature cats you can safely wait 24–48 hours.
- Give small amounts of water only. No milk. If the cat drinks too much at once this could trigger another vomit. Give only a few teaspoonfuls every 30–60 minutes. Or give an ice-block to lick if the cat will cooperate.
- After 12–24 hours, offer a *small* amount of a readily digestible food that you know your cat likes. These foods should prefer-ably be cooked and minced first as this aids digestion. Suitable foods include chicken, mutton and white fish.
- If the first 1–2 teaspoonfuls are accepted and kept down, wait at least an hour and then offer a little more.
- Do not rush things. Success is more likely if you return to the normal diet slowly. Feed little and often for the next two days, then gradually go back to normal routine over the next 2–4 days.
- Avoid rich or indigestible foods such as heart, liver, raw, fatty meat or rich canned foods for 5–7 days.

Medications

Some cats will accept medication without too much fuss. Do not persist in trying to force medication into a cat that has been vomiting if you meet vigorous resistance. You are likely to cause more vomiting.

Preparations such as Kaomagma or others containing kaolin, pectin and antacids can be obtained from a pharmacist. Ask for a children's preparation, and specify that there *must not be any opiates* in the preparation. (Cats react very badly to morphine.)

DIARRHOEA

The cat's bowel motions are normally a little softer and less well formed than, for example, those of a dog. Stools of the consistency of putty are considered quite normal. Diarrhoea is defined as very loose or fluid bowel motions.

Most cats experience mild bouts of diarrhoea from time to time. This need not alarm you. Treatment is not necessary unless the diarrhoea becomes persistent—but it usually clears up spontaneously.

Some causes of mild diarrhoea include:

- Overeating.
- Unfamiliar foods, which are consequently not digested properly.
- Rich foods, such as liver or too much milk.
- Stress. Diarrhoea is quite a common reaction to stresses such as a new cat in the neighbourhood, thunderstorms, overexcitement, or moving house.

Persistent or severe diarrhoea should not be neglected. Diarrhoea can be caused by such a wide range of factors that it would simplify the situation if you can identify what sort of problem your cat has:

- Hypermotility—bowel is moving too fast.
- Malabsorption—food is not being broken down into basic components, which could then be absorbed, or bowel wall is diseased and is unable to absorb foods.
- Infection—by bacteria, virus or parasite.

When to call the vet

- If diarrhoea is accompanied by vomiting.
- If cat is lethargic, listless.
- If there is blood in faeces or vomit.
- If there is severe abdominal pain.
- If diarrhoea persists or returns after home treatment.

Home treatment

Aim to rest the bowel. Give it time to recover. The bowel is capable of rapidly repairing any damage once the irritant has been eliminated.

Withhold all food for 24 hours (8–12 hours for kittens). Exclude any milk or dairy products. provide plenty of clean water instead. Glucose (not sugar) can be added to the water, ½ teaspoon per cup. After a period of fasting, offer a small amount of a bland, easily digested food such as cooked, minced chicken, or white fish, veal, minced hamburger steak (cooked and fat drained) or cooked egg. If the cat will accept it, mix some boiled rice with this food. Select a food your cat is used to and is known to like. Serve it at blood temperature. Give a little, every few hours. Total for the first day should be no more than half the normal ration. Do not rush to get the cat back to normal routine. Take 3–5 days to return gradually to a normal diet.

Medications

- Aluminium hydroxide gel (e.g. Kaomagma, Kaopectate, or Peptosil). Dose: adult ½–1 teaspoon per 5 kg three times a day.
- Activated charcoal: ½–2 tablets daily.
- Yoghurt or concentrated 'good bacteria'.

Chronic diarrhoea

If your cat suffers recurring bouts of diarrhoea, or if the diarrhoea fails to clear up with simple treatment, you should consult your vet. Take a faecal sample with you. Better still, drop a sample in a few days before your visit to allow time for the sample to be examined for the presence of such things as parasite eggs, undigested foods and digestive enzymes.

ENTERITIS

Enteritis is more severe and serious than simple diarrhoea. The lining of the gut wall is damaged—perhaps due to bacterial infection (such as salmonella, clostridia and *E. coli*) or viral infection (such as feline infectious enteritis).

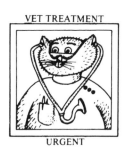

VET TREATMENT

URGENT

Signs

Signs of enteritis include some or all of the following:

- Abdominal pain: the cat assumes a hunched posture and is reluctant to allow you to feel its abdomen. The abdomen is tensed against the anticipated pain of your probing fingers.
- Loose, watery or ill-formed faeces. The cat strains frequently, passing only small quantities of foul-smelling faeces.
- Faeces have a strong, penetrating and offensive smell.
- Bad breath.
- Increased thirst.
- Vomiting.
- Listlessness or extreme lethargy.

Treatment

Veterinary attention is essential.

CONSTIPATION

Constipation is the infre-
quent passage of faeces. As a
result, the faeces become
hard and dry and therefore
difficult or painful to pass.

Normal defaecation

Signs
Because cats tend to be private in their toilet habits,
owners might not detect
this problem until it is well
advanced. Signs you might
note:

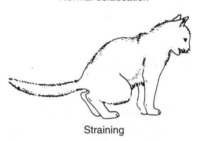

Straining

- Difficulty passing motion.
- Frequent attempts to defaecate: squatting, straining then digging to bury
an imaginary motion.
(*Beware:* this is also a sign
of cystitis, or blocked
bladder, discussed in chapter 15, 'Kidney and bladder'.)
- Dry, hard faeces. Might be blood-flecked.
- Loss of appetite, lethargy and dullness.
- Vomiting.

You might be able to feel the contents of your cat's abdomen.
Constipation is detected as a large sausage-shaped mass lying paral-
lel to the cat's backbone.

Constipation is usually insidious in its onset. It is frequently
detected only when the cat is severely distressed. Constipation is no
joke. It is potentially very serious.

Causes
Cats vary in their susceptibility to constipation. Most cats are never
bothered. With others, constant supervision is required to prevent
it. Causes of constipation include diet, age, hair, lack of exercise,
and injuries.

Dry foods can predispose to constipation, especially if the fluid
intake is inadequate. Most dry foods contain adequate amounts of
fibre. Some do not. Bones are very constipating. If your cat likes
bones, but tends to become constipated, eliminate them from the
diet. All meat diets or primarily meat diets lack sufficient fibre and
can cause constipation.

As cats get older, the bowel muscle tone deteriorates. Some cats become unable to push out faeces.

The shedding of large amounts of hair in spring or when the cat is ill can lead to the formation of hard, coarse faeces wound up in masses of hair.

Fat, lazy indoor cats are far more likely to become constipated than active, outdoor cats. If a cat that is normally allowed to roam outside is shut indoors for an extended period this could lead to constipation as these cats are often reluctant to use litter trays.

Injuries to the pelvis are fairly common in car accidents. The pelvis might be narrowed as a result, which could lead to constipation. Other injuries that make passing faeces painful or difficult include injuries to the back or spine, or to the tail.

Home treatment

The aim of treatment is to lubricate the passage of faeces and/or soften the mass that has already formed. You could try *one* of the following. Do not use them all at once.

- Liquid paraffin (from a pharmacist, not a garage). Dose: ½–1 teaspoon twice daily by mouth.
- Oil emulsions (e.g. Agarol). Dose: ½–1 teaspoon twice daily by mouth.
- Olive oil or other vegetable oils. Dose: 1–2 teaspoons twice daily. Not as effective as liquid paraffin or oil emulsions.
  Note: do not use these oil preparations continuously as they could interfere with absorption of some foods from the bowel, notably some vitamins. Use for a maximum of three days.
- Faecal softeners: e.g. Coloxyl (dioctyl sodium sulphosuccinate). Use a children's preparation. Dose rate is as for a child of 6–12 months or use commercially available cat laxatives. Dose according to manufacturer's instructions.
- Enemas: if drugs fail, an enema might be necessary. An enema is the infusion of a solution into the rectum. It should be performed only by an experienced person. A general anaesthetic is usually given because most cats are unwilling to cooperate with this procedure.

When to call the vet

Call the vet if home treatment is not successful within a day or if the cat is uncomfortable, vomiting or otherwise distressed. *Beware!* What you might think is constipation could be a blocked bladder. This is potentially fatal, so see your vet if the cat is not responding.

Prevention

If your cat is known to be prone to constipation, you might be able to prevent recurrences. First, ensure your cat is getting a properly balanced diet with plenty of fibre. You can increase the amount of fibre in the diet by adding natural, unprocessed bran. Try adding 1 teaspoon a day, then increase or decrease this amount according to the effect.

'Bulk producers' are available commercially. These substances can be added to the cat's food to produce a bulkier, moister stool that is soft and therefore easy to pass. These products can be obtained from your vet or pharmacist. Examples include sterculia granules (normacol) and sorbitol.

If your cat is prone to constipation you should also ensure there is always plenty of water available. Encourage exercise—physically put the cat outside several times a day if necessary.

EXCESSIVE WIND

The production of some gas in the bowel is normal. Passing large volumes of foul-smelling gas from the anus is not. Most of the gases produced in the bowel are absorbed into the blood stream and eventually eliminated, mainly through the lungs. If too much gas is produced, some will leak out of the anus ('flatus' or 'farting'). The control of this excessive gas is usually easy, but some cases frustrate all efforts of treatment.

The first step is usually to change the cat's diet. Some foods result in the formation of large volumes of gas, for example, uncooked carbohydrates, peas, beans and other legumes, slightly tainted meat and some vegetables. Review your cat's diet and remove any suspect foods. Feed less at each meal. Small meals are

more likely to be properly digested, with a consequent reduction in the amount of gas produced. Feed 3–4 small meals a day. Change your brand of cat food. Some cause a lot more gas production than others. Also add yoghurt or lactobacilli to the diet.

Some old cats have poor muscle tone in their bowel, which makes it harder for them to restrain the passage of gas through the gut. This could result in the intermittent, uncontrolled passage of foul gases. These cases are harder to solve. A general effort to improve your cat's overall health is worthwhile—vitamin and mineral supplementation, worming, good diet and so on.

Sometimes medications help. Activated charcoal mixed with the food absorbs surprisingly large volumes of gas. Unfortunately, few cats will accept food medicated with charcoal. The addition of a small amount of natural, unflavoured yoghurt may help.

Your vet may supply you with preparations that slow bowel motility. Perhaps there is a chronic bowel infection that could be treated with antibiotics, or a chronic parasite problem that should be dealt with.

INDIGESTIBLE OBJECTS SWALLOWED

Cats are careful about what they eat. Adult cats rarely swallow potentially dangerous objects. They might, however, inadvertently swallow indigestible items such as hard-shelled insects or small birds. Kittens, on the other hand, due to their natural curiosity are more liable to swallow indigestible objects such as string, wool, small balls, foam rubber and so on. Eating cotton can lead to serious consequences if there is a needle on the other end. Fortunately, needles are usually swallowed blunt end first. The needle might pass right through the gut, or it might lodge in the throat or neck, or it might preforate the gut.

If you know or suspect that your cat has swallowed an indigestible object seek veterinary attention.

Indigestible objects can lead to obstruction of the bowel. Never pull on a piece of string or cotton hanging out of the cat's anus. You could cause further damage, such as pulling a needle through the bowel wall.

OBSTRUCTIONS OF THE BOWEL

Possible causes of bowel obstruction include:
• Indigestible foreign body such as insect shells.

- Pieces of rubber, or plastic and bits of polystyrene foam.
- Balled up string, cotton or foam.
- Twist in the bowel, or a telescoping of the gut into itself (intussusception), which can be a sequel to acute gut infections or inflammation or to heavy worm burdens.

Signs

The signs depend on where the obstruction is and whether it completely blocks the bowel. It might only cause a partial blockage.

In the case of a total obstruction of the stomach or small intestine, the signs are dramatic and could include the following:

- Vomiting.
- Acute depression/listlessness.
- Tense, painful abdomen.
- Disinclination to move. Hunched appearance.
- Body temperature may fall due to shock (feet and ears feel cold to touch).

If the obstruction is partial or is in the large bowel, the signs are less noticeable. They could include some or all of the following:

- Listlessness, depression, lethargy.
- Foul breath.
- Loss of appetite.
- No, or few, bowel motions.
- Occasional vomiting, perhaps faecal in character.
- Dehydration (dry, tacky skin).

Diagnosis

Your vet might be able to feel the obstruction, or might X-ray the cat or even perform an exploratory operation if the cat is in severe distress.

Treatment

Seek urgent veterinary treatment.

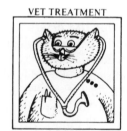

VET TREATMENT

URGENT

PANCREATITIS

The pancreas is an unspectacular organ until something goes wrong with it. The pancreas lies alongside the stomach, nestling close to the duodenum. It has two functions: to produce insulin, and to produce digestive enzymes, which are essential for the digestion of food in the bowel. The pancreas and the liver are the key organs in digestion.

Acute pancreatitis

If the pancreas becomes damaged or inflamed, its cells break apart, releasing the digestive enzymes they contain. Unfortunately, the pancreas itself is not immune to the action of these enzymes. The pancreas literally starts to digest itself, a condition called acute pancreatitis. This is is dangerous. If the damage is extensive and a large volume of enzymes is released, the entire pancreas can be affected. Acute pancreatitis is extremely painful and potentially fatal.

Causes

In most cases, we don't know. Some are started by bacterial infection, some by penetration of a foreign body such as a needle, some by viral infection. In many cases there is is no apparent trigger.

Signs

* Acute, debilitating pain.
* Cat might adopt a 'praying' position in an effort to minimise pain.
* Vomiting; might pass loose, yellow faeces.
* Shock: pale gums, rapid weak pulse.
* Cat reluctant to move.

Treatment

Your vet will attempt to ease the inflammation in the pancreas and alleviate the pain. Most respond well, but treatment is not always successful.

After the crisis

If the damage to the pancreas has been extensive you will have to be careful what you feed your cat. The aim is to feed small amounts of readily digestible foods. Supplementary pancreatic enzymes are available and can be mixed with the food before serving it. Your vet will give you a suitable diet, telling you what you can and cannot give.

Avoid fatty foods and sudden changes in diet. Stick to a fairly bland diet. The wrong diet can precipitate relapses.

Chronic pancreatitis

Chronic pancreatitis is not a dramatic condition. The pancreas gradually becomes less productive for a variety of poorly understood reasons. It gradually produces less and less until there are not sufficient enzymes for efficient digestion.

Sometimes bouts of acute pancreatitis gradually reduce the amount of functional pancreas tissue. In most cases there has been no known history of bouts of acute pancreatitis, although many owners report that, in hindsight, the cat did have episodes of being off food for a few days. These episodes could have been mild bouts of pancreatitis, insufficient to cause overt signs of pain but enough to reduce gradually the pancreas' output.

The clinical signs are not of a painful abdominal crisis but of maldigestion.

Signs
- Weight loss (or failure to gain weight).
- Ill-formed bowel motions—greasy, yellowish but could become rancid and foul-smelling.
- Undigested food in faeces (usually need to detect this micro-scropically).

Treatment
Pancreas enzymes are commercially available to supplement the cat's own pancreas production and to increase the pancreas enzymes to a level to allow normal digestion. Fortunately they have become relatively inexpensive. They are mixed with the cat's food. Response to treatment can be excellent.

DIABETES

There are two forms of diabetes. *Diabetes insipitus* is rare, and *Diabetes mellitus*, although not common, has been increasing in frequency.

Diabetes insipitus
In this form of diabetes, the cat's kidneys are unable to concentrate the body's waste products into a relatively small volume of urine. As a result, the cat produces vast quantities of weak urine.

Diabetes mellitus

In this condition the pancreas fails to produce enough insulin. Insulin is essential for the cells to be able to utilise their basic energy source, glucose. Insulin enables glucose to enter the cell.

Without the presence of insulin the cells cannot get glucose from the bloodstream. Because they lack glucose within their cell walls, they signal for more. The body responds to this apparent glucose lack by releasing more. The level of glucose in the blood-stream rises higher and higher. The cells are oblivious to the potential amount of glucose available. Without insulin, it is useless to them. The level of glucose in the blood eventually rises so high that the kidney cannot retain it all. Glucose starts to spill out into the urine. This urine is 'sweet' due to its high glucose content. The ancient Greeks noted the sweetness of a diabetic's urine—hence the name *mellitus*, Greek for 'sweet'.

Signs
Clinical signs include all or some of the following:
- Increased urine output.
- Frequency of urinating.
- Thirst.
- Hunger.
- Weight loss.
Blood and urine tests show abnormal levels of glucose.

Treatment
Diabetes in cats can sometimes be treated with diet restriction. In other cases daily insulin injections are required. The amount of insulin to be given is at first determined by your vet and then adminstered and monitored by you at home. Insulin dosage is adjusted according to urine testing and/or monitoring water and food intake as well as observing the cat's behaviour. It is important to keep accurate records of these things.

Treatment of your diabetic cat will require an excellent working relationship with your vet, patience and determination. But it can be done!

LIVER DISEASE

The liver is the powerhouse of the body. It manufactures and stores the basic food until required by the body, manufactures essential vitamins, stores minerals and vitamins, breaks down toxins and poisons and produces digestive enzymes and bile.

Hepatitis means 'inflamed liver'. There are many causes of hepatitis from poisoning to bacterial or viral infection. In humans, the term *hepatitis* is commonly understood to mean the infectious viral form. These particular viruses do not affect cats. Nor can humans contact the feline 'hepatitis'.

Signs

The liver has remarkable reserves of functional tissue, so signs of liver injury may not become apparent until extensive damage has been done. The liver has such a wide range of functions that the clinical signs of liver disease (hepatitis) are quite varied. Laboratory tests are usually required to confirm a diagnosis.

Some signs that might be associated with liver disease include:
- Vomiting.
- Pain in abdomen, especially on right side under the rib cage.
- Swollen abdomen.
- Diarrhoea (especially a greasy, yellowish stool).
- Listlessness.
- Jaundice (yellowing of the visible mucous membranes, the gums, conjuctiva, lips of vulva).
- Dark-coloured urine.

Causes

Causes of liver disease include:
- Poisoning.
- Bacterial and viral infection.
- Cirrhosis (scarring of the liver).
- Cancer (often seeded or 'secondary' tumours).
- Heart disease.
- Fatty infiltration of liver.
- Damage by toxins absorbed from other parts of body, for example the gut.

Diagnosis

Blood, faecal and other tests could be needed before treatment is proceeded with. X-rays might be helpful. Sometimes exploratory surgery is indicated, especially if a tumour or obstruction is suspected.

Treatment

Veterinary treatment is essential. Treatment can be complicated and prolonged. On recovery, it will be essential to provide your cat with a diet that puts the minimum of strain on the liver's resources. These are available commercially, or you might want to prepare your own.

The following diet is called a 'liver protection diet':
1½ cups cottage cheese
½ cup cooked, drained rice
1 large hard-boiled egg
2 teaspoons brewer's yeast

3 teaspoons glucose
1 teaspoon maize/corn oil
1 teaspoon potassium chloride (KCL), also called 'No Salt'
2 teaspoons DCP powder
Feed a small amount (1–2 tablespoonsful) several times daily.

The major drawback of this diet is that many cats won't eat it. You might have to increase the protein or introduce meat.

If all else fails, feed the cat according to these rules:

- Give a little, often.
- Avoid fats.
- Give lean, white meats (chicken, rabbit, fish) in preference to rich, red meat (beef, lamb).
- Give a daily vitamin and mineral supplement.

ANAL SACS AND GLANDS

The cat has two small sacs located on each side of its anus. These are sometimes called scent glands. They contain an extremely foul-smelling secretion. A little of this secretion is expressed on to each bowel motion. Their function is presumably to mark the droppings with the cat's own individual scent. This aids in boundary or territorial marking, or in identifying the presence of a new cat in the area.

Problems occasionally arise if these anal sacs become over-full, which occurs if the duct through which they empty becomes blocked. Secretions

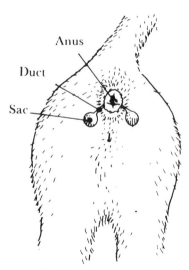

Position of the anal sacs

then build up within the sac, and the subsequent swelling in the sensitive perineal region causes discomfort to the cat.

The secretions within the sacs can dry up (become impacted/inspissated) and therefore difficult or impossible to pass. This condition is sometimes associated with chronic constipation as the sacs are not emptied regularly. The reverse can also occur if the sacs are swollen and painful; the cat finds it painful to pass faeces, and therefore becomes constipated.

Signs

- Cat licks anxiously under the tail.
- Rubbing bottom along the floor.
- Suddenly turning round to look at the tail (as if pricked by a needle).
- A swelling, redness or a discharge in the area around and beneath the anus.

Treatment

Unless an infection has developed, the sacs can be expressed by manually squeezing them. Your vet will show you how to do this. It is simple enough but be gentle, and *beware!* The secretions from the anal sacs can be ejected unexpectedly and with considerable velocity. They are extremely foul-smelling.

The anal sacs can also become infected and fill with pus. An abscess can develop, causing a painful swelling below and to one side of the anus. These abscesses usually burst, leaving a ragged opening that discharges a little pus or a blood-stained fluid.

If anal sac problems are severe or recurring, your vet might advise surgical removal of the glands. The cat suffers no apparent handicap from their loss.

INTERNAL PARASITES

Several types of internal parasites (or worms) live in the intestines of cats: roundworms, hookworms and tapeworms.

Roundworms

Roundworms (*toxocara cati, toxascaris leonina*) are a *very* common parasite of kittens. Adult cats can also be affected. All kittens should be treated for roundworms.

Roundworms are quite large. They can grow up to 18 cm in length, although they are usually less than half that.

Infestation

Kittens can become infested with roundworm by eating roundworm eggs, which can be present in vast numbers around the nest at birth. Large numbers of eggs can be stuck to the mother's fur and skin, especially around the nipples. The kittens ingest these while suckling. Eggs can also be ingested through contaminated foods, or while the kitten is grooming.

Adults can be infested when they eat food contaminated with the sticky roundworm eggs, or when they eat prey such as mice, birds and some insects. These are called intermediate hosts. These intermediate hosts have swallowed roundworm eggs, which then encyst within their body and so remain potent until the cat preys on them.

Q *What harm do roundworms do?*

In small numbers they cause little harm. Larger numbers can cause irritation and thickening of the gut wall, which interferes with proper digestion and absorption of food. Intermittent diarrhoea can result. Kittens fail to thrive and might develop a disintended pot belly.

The larvae of one of the roundworms (*T. cati*) migrates through the liver and lungs as part of the lifecycle. If sufficient numbers of larvae are involved, significant damage can be inflicted on the liver and lungs.

Diagnosis

Because roundworm is so common in kittens, many vets recommend the routine worming of all kittens without necessarily getting a positive diagnosis of infestation first.

If a diagnosis is required, a laboratory examination of the cat's faeces will detect microscopic roundworm eggs, if the kitten has egg-laying adults in its intestine. It takes about two months for an egg to develop into a mature egg-laying adult worm. Young kittens could therefore have a heavy burden of immature worms without having eggs in their droppings. So *beware!* A 'negative' faecal test does not necessarily mean that the kitten does not have worms.

Treatment

Treatment of kittens should start as early as 4–6 weeks of age. Treat the kittens every 2–4 weeks until 5 months old and then every 6–8 weeks until 12 months old. Adult cats should be treated 3–4 times a year. Pregnant queens should be treated at least once in the last three weeks of their pregnancy. Ask your vet to recommend a drug, especially if you are using it for a pregnant queen or for young kittens.

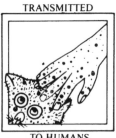
TRANSMITTED

TO HUMANS

Young pups are more dangerous as a source of roundworm than kittens. Nevertheless—be sure to worm your kitten regularly.

Children could pick up roundworm eggs, especially when stroking young kittens or a recently queened female. These eggs can also be picked up from sandpits or garden areas where cats defaecate. Finger-sucking toddlers are especially at risk. These roundworm eggs might develop into larvae that can migrate through the intestine and into organs such as the liver where they can cause serious damage. It is possible for them to reach and injure the eye and brain. The larvae never develop into adult worms, so—contrary to common belief—children do not develop worms from cats (or dogs).

Preventive measures
- Treat your cat for roundworm on a regular basis, e.g. every three months.
- Be certain children wash their hands after handling kittens or queen; *or* don't allow them to play with the kittens at all.
- Sandpits should be covered when not in use to prevent them from becoming toilet areas for cats.

Hookworms

Hookworms (*ancylostoma* spp., *uncinaria* spp.) are only small worms— 1–2 cm long—but they can cause serious damage to the cat's delicate intestinal lining. Some are blood suckers. Others feed on the intestine's surface. *Ancylstoma* species, found mainly in summer rainfall areas, are vigorous blood suckers. *Uncinaria* species, found mainly in winter rainfall areas, are milder in their effects, although heavy infestations are debilitating and cause intestinal upsets.

Infestation
There are several ways a cat can become infested with roundworm:
- In a moist, unhygienic environment, the hookworm larvae burrow into the skin, migrate to the blood vessels and are swept into the lungs. After moving into the bronchi they are coughed up, then swallowed. The larvae mature into adults and take up residence in the cat's small intestine.
- Eating food contaminated with larvae.
- Infection can occur even before the kitten is born, although this is very rare. The larvae migrate into the uterus to infect the unborn kitten.

Signs
- Diarrhoea. Mainly dark, loose, might be bloody.
- Weight loss.
- General loss of condition, including poor coat, listlessness.
- Dermatitis due to invasion of larvae through skin.

Many cats show no clinical signs at all. A routine faecal examination annually at vaccination time will enable treatment where necessary.

These signs vary in degree according to the age and condition of the cat and with the number of worms parasitising it.

Diagnosis

Your vet will examine a sample of faeces for the presence of distinctive hookworm eggs.

Treatment

It is not sufficient merely to kill the worms in the cat's bowel. You must also prevent reinfestation. With all those hookworm eggs already in the ground, preventing reinfestation requires a plan to counter the probability of a new build-up of hookworm.

If the cat has already been affected severely, feed good-quality food and include a reliable iron, vitamin and mineral supplement to help counter the anaemia caused by the hookworm.

Where hookworm is a problem in kittens, treatment can commence as early as 4–6 weeks of age. If the kittens have been diagnosed as having hookworm, initially treatment is required every 3 weeks for a minimum of 3 doses. In kittens older than 3 months, treatment every 3 months is sufficient to keep the numbers down.

Initially, treat adult cats 3 times at intervals of 21 days. Adult cats usually develop a good immunity to reinfestation with hookworm, so treatment once every summer is adequate as a routine.

Always read the label carefully before giving a cat drugs for hookworm. Some preparations that are suitable for dogs are toxic for cats. If unsure, check with your veterinarian.

Tapeworms

There are many different types of tapeworm. All consist of a head, which attaches to the wall of the intestine, and a body composed of segments that look like many barrels stacked end to end. The hindmost segments contain many thousands of eggs, which are intermittently shed in the cat's faeces. Some tapeworm reach sizes of more than a metre long but most are only a few centimetres long. Surprisingly, perhaps, tapeworm usually cause very little trouble except in old or delibilated cats. In an otherwise healthy cat, the tapeworm is tolerated well. Occasionally tapeworm can cause a mild bowel upset, with diarrhoea or constipation. The tapeworm segments pass out of the anus where they might stick to the hairs around the anus resulting in an itchy bottom. In these cases, the cat vigorously licks under its tail. Look for dried tapeworm segments. They resemble flattened dried up grains of rice.

Tapeworm

Cat tapeworm are not dangerous to humans. People can get flea tapeworm, but it is not a serious disease. It is the dog hydatid tapeworm that is a human health hazard.

Infection
Tapeworm are not passed directly from cat to cat. To complete the lifecycle, the egg must be eaten by an intermediate host such as a flea, bird, mouse or rat. Further development takes place within this intermediate host. When a cat subsequently eats the intermediate host, the cycle is completed. The worm develops into an adult in the cat's intestine. The cat can also be infected by eating fresh raw meat. Meat should be cooked or frozen and thawed before being fed to your cat.

Diagnosis
Look for segments in the cat's faeces or attached to the hair around the anus. As fleas are a source of reinfestation, flea control is important.

COCCIDIOSIS

Coccidia are microscopic parasites of the cat's bowel. Small numbers can be present without causing the cat any inconvenience. In the occasional case, significant numbers are present and a chronic diarrhoea may develop, resulting in weight loss and signs that the cat is not flourishing physically. This is most likely to occur in kittens kept in crowded, unhygienic conditions on wet bedding, for example, in some pet shops.

Diagnosis
Diagnosis is by laboratory examination of faecal samples.

Treatment
Response to treatment with sulphonamides is usually good. Your vet will prescribe the correct dose. The environment must be cleaned, disinfected and dried. Disinfection can be achieved with sodium hydroxide, ammonia or other alkaline disinfectants.

15 KIDNEYS AND BLADDER

LE TOILET

THE KIDNEYS

The cat has two kidneys. Their function is to filter the blood and remove wastes. The by-products of normal body metabolism are potentially toxic, and must be constantly flushed from the body. If the kidneys fail, the resulting build-up of toxic wastes has a serious and ultimately fatal effect.

Chronic kidney disease

Chronic kidney disease is the most common condition to threaten the health of the ageing cat. Early recognition of warning signs can allow you to take measures that will prolong kidney function. This helps to keep your cat comfortable for months or even years longer than would be the case if the condition was not recognised and checked.

Signs

Signs do not start until about two-thirds of both kidneys are non-functional. Even though the kidneys have deteriorated only gradually over months or even years, the signs of disease often appear suddenly.

Signs will include some of the following:

- Increased thirst.
- Increased urine production—the cat might start urinating during the night.
- Appetite might increase or decrease—usually it decreases, because the cat is feeling ill.
- Listlessness—physical and mental depression.
- The coat becomes rough and unkempt.
- Weight loss—it is usually insidious and often is not noticed until quite a lot of condition is lost.

- Bad breath.
- Mouth ulcers.
- Vomiting and loose, often dark-coloured faeces.
- Joint and muscle pain and stiffness (not very common).

Causes

As the kidney gradually deteriorates it becomes less efficient. It can no longer extract all the normal by-products and wastes of daily body metabolism from the bloodstream. In order to flush out these potential poisons, the cat must produce greater quantities of dilute urine. This means a loss of body fluids so the cat drinks more to compensate. For this reason one of the first signs of kidney disease is usually an increased thirst.

Drinking more helps only for a while, but gradually the toxic wastes build up. The body tries to expel them through other routes such as in the saliva or through the bowel wall. One of these waste products is urea, which is produced when protein is digested. When large amounts of urea are present in the saliva, the oral bacteria react with it to produce ammonia, which can result in bad breath. Ammonia is an irritant and could also cause mouth ulcers.

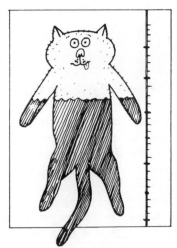

Toxic wastes gradually build up

Increased blood levels of urea and other wastes can cause loss of appetite, nausea, vomiting and listlessness. Anaemia might develop because of toxic depression of the bone marrow, meaning that fewer red blood cells are produced.

Other changes take place in the bloodstream. There are disturbances in the levels of the vital body salts (sodium, potassium, calcium and others). When the kidney is healthy it maintains an exact and delicate balance of these salts. The damaged kidney cannot. As calcium is lost, replacement calcium is leached from the bones, gradually rendering them softer and weaker. If this process is prolonged, some cats develop lameness or could even fracture bones as they become increasingly fragile.

Diagnosis

The signs and history are suggestive, but your vet might want to do tests to confirm a tentative diagnosis. Urine tests are useful, but it is often hard to get a sample from a cat. Blood tests are usually taken. One useful test is to measure the level of a waste product, such as urea, in the blood. There is normally some urea in the bloodstream, but if the kidney is failing this level rises and so gives your vet some idea of how much kidney function remains and therefore what the prognosis for the cat is.

Treatment

Initial treatment by your vet might include:

- Antibiotics—to control any infection present.
- Vitamins—to overcome deficiencies and to help in tissue repair.
- Anabolic steroids—to help stop tissue breakdown.
- Fluids—at critical times these will be injected intravenously or under the skin.

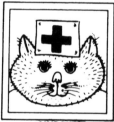

NURSING

Peritoneal dialysis, a technique whereby sophisticated machines are used to remove wastes from the bloodstream, is used on humans but is not feasible for cats.

After the cat comes home you will have to follow up the treatment with good nursing and careful feeding.

Diet

The most important part of home treatment is a correct diet. The aim of this diet is to reduce the amount of protein fed as this reduces the amount of wastes formed. Unfortunately, many cats will refuse any dietary change.

In all cases of kidney failure you should feed little and often instead of giving one or two relatively large meals daily. This spreads the 'workload' of the kidney.

In some countries a commercially produced low protein diet is available for cats with kidney disease. If it is not available the following diet might be acceptable. This diet is high in energy to reduce the cat's need to break down protein.

Example of a restricted protein diet (14% protein):

2 cups cooked rice

1 cooked egg

30 gm liver

2 teaspoons maize oil

½ teaspoon calcium carbonate

½ teaspoon iodised salt

This quantity yields 500 g. A cat weighing 2 kg will need 170 g daily; a 5 kg cat will need 350 g daily.

This diet will be unpalatable to many cats. You might have to raise the protein content until it is acceptable. Add some lean meat, preferably 'white' meat such as chicken or fish. Avoid rich red meats.

Vitamin and mineral supplements should be given daily—especially the B group vitamins A and C. Multivitamin/mineral supplements help to overcome deficiencies and excess losses, and are also helpful in tissue maintenance and repair and in stimulating appetite. Calcium, vitamin B complex and vitamin C supplements are particularly needed. (Brewer's yeast is an excellent source of B vitamins.)

Other home care

Table salt should be added to the diet. It replaces the excessive amounts of sodium lost in the urine, and it also encourages drinking. Sodium bicarbonate (bicarbonate of soda) can be used instead of salt. Add a total of ¼ teaspoon daily in small amounts at a time.

Free access to clean water should always be allowed. Milk is not enough.

Warmth, avoiding stress (even just moving the furniture around can stress some cats) and tender loving care can make a big difference to the outcome of treatment. Try lots of it.

Acute kidney disease

Acute (sudden) kidney disease is not as common as the chronic form and affects mainly younger cats (1–5 years old).

Causes

Some possible causes include:

- Bacterial or viral infection.
- Toxic injury, including ethylene glycol (anti-freeze), carbon tetrachloride, lead, thallium, arsenic, tetrachloroethylene, drugs (some antibiotics), and mercury.
- Shock: the blood supply to the kidney can be drastically affected in shock states, for example after a car accident. Kidney damage occurs due to oxygen lack.

- Snakebite.*
- Severe injury to other parts of the body or major surgery.*
- Accidents (such as a motor car accident) causing bruising or rupture of the kidney.

* In these states damaged blood cells and other debris and waste in the bloodstream can be trapped in the kidney and clog it up.

Signs
Some or all of the following:
- Loss of appetite.
- Abdominal pain, especially in the mid-back area.
- Increased or decreased thirst or apparent attraction to water. The cat might stand over the water bowl without actually drinking.
- Increased or decreased urine output (despite increased thirst).
- Vomiting.
- Dehydration.
- Urine changes—often has a strong smell, might contain blood or pus.

Treatment
If treatment is commenced early the damage can often be restricted. A return to efficient function is possible in many cases. Treatment can include:
- Fluids—could be given intravenously, under the skin or orally.
- Antibiotics (if bacteria are involved).
- Vitamins, especially B group and C.
- Antiemetics—to stop vomiting and reduce fluid loss.

Diet
Your vet will prescribe a diet to follow while the kidneys heal, probably one similar to that given for chronic kidney disease.

THE BLADDER

The bladder is a distendable muscular sack or reservoir used to store the urine formed by the kidneys until the cat is ready to eliminate it. Although the bladder is a relatively simple structure, things can go wrong. When they do, the result is often acutely uncomfortable.

Cystitis

Cystitis, meaning inflammation of the bladder wall, is relatively common condition in the cat and one that can cause great irritation and distress.

Causes

Many cases of cystitis are associated with the formation of a coarse, sand-like deposit. This is explained below in the section on FUS.

Bacterial infection is probably the most common cause of cystitis. Some bacteria are normally present in urine but do not cause problems under normal circumstances. It is when these bacteria are able to multiply, or if particularly pathogenic bacteria gain entry, that cystitis flares up.

The factors that favour bacterial cystitis include:

- Urine stagnation: an important feature of the bladder's defence system is that it empties almost completely. Cats should urinate three or more times daily, literally flushing out bacteria and wastes before they have time to do any damage. If the cat cannot (or will not) empty its bladder regularly, bacteria have a much better chance of multiplying to gain a foothold. Such a situation could occur if the cat does not get out to empty its bladder. For example, the cat might be reluctant to go outside if it is raining or too cold. Or there might be a partial obstruction of the bladder or perhaps a disturbance of bladder function, for example due to spinal injury.
- Physical irritation of bladder wall from bladder stones.
- Irritation due to the bladder worm (these worms only rarely cause problems).

Signs

The first sign is usually that your cat begins to urinate more often, sometimes in unusual places such as in the bath or sink. Only small quantities of urine are passed at each attempt. As the condition develops, the cat spends more and more time squatting and straining, perhaps scratching at the ground, twitching its tail and looking around anxiously. The urine is sometimes bloodstained and might have a strong, offensive odour. The staining can easily be mistaken for a sign of constipation. Many owners waste valuable time treating these cats with oil or purgatives.

Most cats remain fairly bright and continue to eat. Most drink more.

Sometimes the cat does become listless and ill, and might vomit and run a fever.

VET TREATMENT

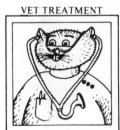

URGENT

Treatment

Your vet will decide on the treatment according to the individual case. Treatment includes:

- Antibiotics if infection is present or suspected.
- Urine acidifiers to reduce new stone formation and suppress bacterial growth.
- Changes to the cat's routine. There are two aims: (1) to get your cat to urinate as often as possible, and (2) prevent the urine becoming too concentrated:
  1 Allow your cat free access to a toilet area. If it uses a litter tray, keep it clean. Some cats are so fastidious that they will not use it once it is too soiled. If the cat uses an outside toilet area, make sure it goes out at least three times daily. In some cases you might have to pick it up physically and put it out. Encourage exercise, as this also increases bladder emptying.
  2 To prevent the urine becoming too concentrated, encourage drinking. Always allow free access to fresh water. Add salt to the food daily (⅛–¼ teaspoon daily). If your cat likes milk, water it down before you give it. Feed sloppy foods as part of the diet. Avoid dry foods. They play a significant role in producing concentrated urine. Some dry foods are high in magnesium and should be avoided for this reason. (See the section on FUS below.)

Feline urolithiasis syndrome

Feline urolithiasis syndrome (FUS) is also known as 'blocked bladder'. The word *urolith* means 'bladder stone'. It is a source of amazement to many that 'stones' can actually grow in the bladder and kidney. These stones are aggregations of minerals that form into tiny crystals or into sand-like grains or even into large masses several centimetres across. If they form in the kidney they are called kidney stones. In the cat they usually form in the bladder, and are known as feline urolithiasis syndrome or, more commonly, bladder stones.

There are many different types of bladder and kidney stones. Their cause, the type of damage produced and the correct treatment vary with their composition and positions. In people, kidney stones are the most common type. In the cat, by far the more common site is the bladder. Usually a sludge of a sand-like precipitate forms rather than a discrete 'stone'. This sand irritates the bladder wall, causing cystitis. In male cats it can cause a blockage of the bladder if it builds up to plug the urethra (see diagram). Because the urethra of the female cat is relatively much wider it is less liable to become blocked.

Signs

Where there is cystitis and maybe a partial bladder block, the first signs are:

- Cat spends a lot of time in one spot, often the litter tray or a favourite toilet area.
- Straining (could be mistaken for constipation).
- Twitching tail.
- Licking penis or area under tail.

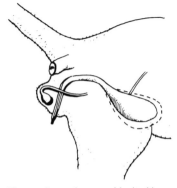

The penis can become blocked by a plug of precipitate (struvite)

Later signs develop if the bladder becomes completely blocked and the cat is unable to urinate:

- Penis might be protruded, swollen and red or congested with blood, turning it a blue or blackish colour.
- Tense, painful abdomen. Cat might have difficulty walking.
- Dark, blood-tinged urine might be passed in small amounts.
- Cat becomes listless, physically and mentally depressed.
- Loss of appetite.
- Vomiting.
- Howling in pain.

It is easy to misdiagnose your cat's condition as constipation, and many owners waste valuable time giving oil or laxatives. This delay reduces the chances of a favourable outcome.

A blocked bladder is an emergency. The cat will die without treatment.

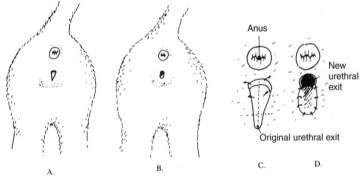

Perineal urethrostomy: This operation results in the elimination of the narrowest part of the urethra, where blockages usually occur. (A) The penis is blocked; (B) After surgery, the penis is partly amputated and partly opened up; (C) Penis before surgery. The tip is removed. The rest is opened, folded back; (D) The new exit for urine is higher up, much wider and less liable to blockage

Treatment

The vet must relieve the obstruction and re-establish the free passage of urine. This previously required the administration of a general anaesthetic and the passage of a fine tube (a catheter) into the bladder, which can be difficult. In severe or recurring cases your vet might advise a surgical procedure to eliminate the dangerous bottleneck in the penis where blockages usually occur. The most common procedure is called a perineal urethrostomy. In our experience, the outlook after surgery is usually excellent.

A change of diet to a commercial product that dissolves the crystals and then to another diet to prevent recurrence has revolutionised the treatment of this condition and has rendered perineal urethrostomy unnecessary in all but a few cases.

Prevention

If any infection is present it will have to be eliminated, usually through antibiotics. Drugs that acidify the urine are useful in some cases. The main preventive measures concern the cat's diet.

The primary aim is to prevent the formation of concentrated urine and to prevent urine retention. Eliminating dry foods from the diet of cats suffering from FUS is a high priority, unless it is a specially formulated dietary food.

In the majority of cases the substances precipitated in the bladder and urethra is a complex called struvite, an important element of which is magnesium. Research shows that diets high in magnesium are more likely to result in struvite formation. It follows that cats with a history of struvite formation should not be given diets high in magnesium. Foods high in magnesium include beef, heart, pork, cod, herring, kippers, pilchards, and sardines.

Other measures

Other useful preventive measures include encouraging a high water intake, encouraging the cat to pass urine frequently, urine acidifiers and special commercial foods.

It is not always possible to encourage a high water intake, but try the following measures:
- Allow free access to clean water.
- Add some table salt daily to the cat's rations. About ¼ teaspoon daily is usually effective in increasing the cat's thirst.
  To encourage the cat to pass urine frequently:
- Allow free access to the litter tray or an outside toilet area.
- Encourage exercise, which might mean physically putting the cat out at least three times daily or playing games that get the cat moving about.

In some cases, using drugs (such as methionine) that increase the acidity of urine will slow the formation of new stones and might even dissolve those already formed. They are more effective if they are not given continually; a short course every few weeks is often more effective.

Several types of commercial food that either treat the condition or prevent its recurrence are now available. Ask your vet to recommend foods that produce an acid urine. They are freely available and are very effective.

The bladder worm

The bladder worm (*cappilaria feliscati*) is quite common in some areas. It is a very fragile, thread-like worm measuring 1–6 cm long. It is difficult to see with the naked eye. Most infestations cause no problem, although in rare cases the worms irritate the bladder wall enough to produce cystitis. Treatment is usually unnecessary.

Urinary incontinence

Urinary incontinence (dribbling) is not a common problem in the cat. Possible causes include:
* Inborn abnormality.
* As a sequel to persistent bouts of FUS or chronic cystitis.
* Loss of nervous control, due to spinal damage or after trauma such as a car accident.
* A hormonal imbalance (in females).

Signs
The cat either constantly drips small amounts of urine or occasionally unconsciously passes urine, often during sleep or when lying resting.

Treatment
The treatment depends on the cause. Urine incontinence is always a case for your vet, not for home treatment. If urinary incontinence persists there is a high risk of bacterial infection spreading up into the bladder.

16 HEART AND LUNGS

THE HEART

The heart is a pump. It is composed of specialised muscle that expands and contracts, tirelessly, throughout the cat's life. The heart must keep the blood constantly circulating throughout the body, supplying oxygen and nutrients and removing wastes, warming or cooling, keeping the body in harmony.

Heart disease in cats is not common, especially in comparison with the incidence in humans.

The normal heart rate for cats is fast: 100 to 240 beats per minute.

Heart failure and disease

If the heart fails to perform effectively, the blood is not circulated efficiently and the entire body is affected. The clinical signs of heart failure are a result of this poor blood flow.

Causes of heart disease

The exact cause of heart disease for each individual patient is often not determined. Some of the possible causes include:

- Heart muscle deterioration, with fibrosis or scarring of the heart muscle ('cardiomyopathy'). This can occur even in young cats.
- Deterioration in the circulation in the heart muscle itself.
- Heart valve disease. The major chambers of the heart are closed off by valves. If these valves become

Exercise intolerance can be an early warning sign

leaky, due perhaps to growths on their surfaces, the heart becomes inefficient.

- Infections by bacteria or virus that damage the heart's muscular walls or surrounding sac (pericardium).
- Congenital malformations of the heart or the great vessels.
- Trauma to chest.
- Tumours involving heart or structures near the heart.

Warning signs of heart failure

When the lungs become congested some of the fluid pools in the air passages (the bronchi). The cat intermittently coughs it up, but you will not see it as the cat immediately swallows it. This type of cough is typically a deep moist cough with a 'tinny' sound. It is termed a 'cardiac cough'.

Be suspicious of a deep, moist and resonant cough, particularly in an old cat. At first the 'heart cough' is especially notable in the early morning, or when the cat gets up from a rest and starts to move about. Later, the cough becomes more persistent. The cat will then cough intermittently throughout the day.

As a result of poor circulation fluid pools in the abdomen, giving the cat a pot-bellied appearance.

The cat with heart disease tires easily and is reluctant to exercise, spending most of the day sleeping. If forced into activity, these cats will start to breathe very rapidly and might become breathless. Because cats sleep a lot, this sign could go unnoticed

Some heart patients just can't seem to get comfortable at night. They are restless and seem to be 'on edge'. This is due to the discomfort of congested lungs or a tight, fluid-filled abdomen.

Other possible signs could include:

- Wastage of muscles.
- Pale or bluish-coloured gums (lift the upper lip back to inspect the gums).
- Difficulty breathing or rapid breathing.
- As the cat's condition deteriorates the cat might have episodes of open mouthed gasping.
- Fainting spells.

Treatment

Heart conditions in cats often carry a poor prognosis. It is usually not possible to cure the condition, but it might be possible to control it. Treatment is usually limited to drug therapy to improve the heart's performance as well as good nursing to reduce the workload on the heart. This can be very effective in many cases.

Techniques of heart surgery are advancing dramatically in sophistication and success rate. In veterinary medicine the amount of heart surgery possible is limited by technical and financial constraints, but could be considered in selected cases.

Excessive fluid build-up can be relieved with drugs such as frusemide and other 'diuretics'. These must be used only under veterinary supervision. The performance of the heart muscle can be improved by certain drugs, for example, digoxin, propanolol and the theophyline-like drugs. The selection and dose rates of these drugs must be tailored individually to each case. You should establish a good working relationship with your vet. Ask for an explanation of the actions of any drug prescribed so that you will know when alterations in treatment might be indicated. Owners are usually very good at noting small changes in their cat's condition.

Rest is essential. The cat will usually look after this aspect of treatment quite satisfactorily. You can help by avoiding stress situations that could make the cat anxious or tense. These stresses include things *you* might not think of as stressful. For example, putting the cat outside at night could be stressful if there are other cats about (especially toms). They might threaten your cat. Other stress situations are more obvious. Don't let the dog or young children romp around or tease the cat. And this is certainly *not* the time to acquire a new pet in an attempt to cheer up the ailing cat. Such an invader of the cat's domain is likely to make its condition far worse, not better.

The role of diet in the treatment of heart failure is not so critical as for people, but you should restrict salt as much as you can. If your cat also has kidney disease then talk to your vet about how much salt is advisable, as *some* is essential. Most commercial foods are high in salt because it helps to make them palatable. In some countries, specially prepared low-salt cat foods are available for cats with heart disease. Where they are not available you will have to cut down salt by giving more home-cooked or fresh foods and less commercially prepared foods.

Foods that are low in salt include:
- Freshwater fish.
- Chicken (without skin), rabbit, beef, lamb, horsemeat.
- Egg yolk.
- Rice, macaroni, spaghetti.
- Unsalted butter.

Foods that are high in salt and should be avoided include:
- Cheese and other dairy foods.
- Processed meats (including meat blocks, sausage, ham, bacon).
- Most tinned cat foods.

- Heart, kidney and liver.
- Shellfish.

Heartworm

Heartworm is primarily a disease of dogs, but the incidence in cats is much higher than vets originally thought. Unfortunately, diagnosis is difficult, and signs of infection are not consistent. Even a few heartworms in a cat can cause severe damage and even sudden death, whereas dogs tolerate a few worms quite well.

Heartworm are very fine worms, 9–12 cm long. Cats become infected when mosquitoes carrying heartworm larvae feed from them. Male cats and cats that spend a lot of time outside are most likely to be infected.

Signs

The most common signs are coughing, often paroxysmal, and difficulty breathing. Sometimes there is loss of balance, blindness or seizures or even sudden death.

Some chronically affected cats have intermittent signs only, either of episodes of coughing and difficult breathing, or of intermittent chronic vomiting unrelated to eating or drinking.

Diagnosis

Diagnosis is difficult. Blood tests that are very reliable in dogs are quite the opposite in cats. X-rays might help, and clinical signs, especially increased lung sounds and intermittent vomiting, might be suggestive.

Treatment

Controversy surrounds treatment for heartworm as its effectiveness is questionable and the side effects might cause further problems. The condition is far more amenable to treatment in dogs than in cats.

Prevention

Treatment once a month with a specific preventative heartworm medicine (containing ivermectin or other appropriate drug) is 100 per cent effective in preventing infection.

THE LUNGS

The lungs occupy most of the chest. They are supported and protected by the ribs. The heart nestles between the lungs.

Lung disease

The cat has a remarkable capacity to compensate if part of the lungs are damaged. This can mean that there are very few signs of lung disease until the condition has reached an advanced stage at which time most of the cat's lung tissue is affected. By the time the cat shows obvious signs of distress, successful treatment could be very difficult.

Signs

A cat showing some of the following signs could have a lung or bronchial condition:

- Rapid breathing: more than 30 breaths per minute is abnormal, unless the cat is very excited or hot.
- Difficult or painful breathing, which can be signalled by a hunched appearance. The cat typically crouches down with the elbows held out and away from the chest.
- Panting, or breathing with the mouth open: while dogs pant to lose heat, cats don't. Open-mouthed breathing usually indicates that the cat is very distressed, perhaps due to being hot or terrified, or because of serious lung disease.
- Pale or bluish-coloured gums: lift the cat's lips back to expose the gums. The gums should be a healthy pink colour. When the hums have a bluish tinge (termed cyanosis) it means the blood is not getting enough oxygen. When the gums are very pale it might mean anaemia or shock. When the gums are very dark, even blackish, this is usually due only to excessive pigment (skin colouring) and is not a cause for concern.
- Other abnormal breathing sounds, such as snuffling, snorting, bubbling, honking or wheezing.
- Other, less specific signs, could include: discharge from the nose, loss of appetite, a reluctance to get up and move about, fever, general malaise.

Pneumonia

Pneumonia means inflammation of the lungs. The most common cause is infection by bacteria or virus. These bacteria can be inhaled in droplet form from direct contact with another infected cat, or can come via the bloodstream or from a penetrating chest wound. Parasitic invasion, such as lungworm or roundworm larvae, can also lead to pneumonia.

Treatment

The treatment depends on the cause. If bacteria are involved, antibiotics are usually indicated. Viral infections have to run their course, although, because they are frequently complicated by a 'secondary' bacterial infection, antibiotics may be used here also.

Rest is essential. This reduces the stress on the lungs. It might be necessary to confine the cat to a cage or to a small room, thereby forcing it to rest. This is termed 'cage rest' and is the equivalent of human 'bed rest'. In acute cases, oxygen might be given, but this requires special facilities. Good nursing is essential. This includes good feeding, ensuring warmth and rest, proper medication and lots of the all-important TLC. Pneumonia is a serious illness, and effective nursing can make the difference between recovery and failure.

Lungworm

Lungworm is caused by a parasite, *Aelurostrongylus abstrusus*, which is widespread and found in most places, including Europe, the USA and Australia. Infection occurs when the cat eats prey that is infested with lungworm larvae. Such prey can include snails, frogs, slugs, birds, reptiles or rodents.

The main sign of lungworm infection is a cough. This cough is especially severe in the early stages of infection because the young lungworms are relatively active and move around in the lungs, thereby causing a great deal of irritation. The cough gradually becomes less frequent, but deeper and more resonant. If the infestation is severe, the cat's general weight and condition will deteriorate. Other signs can include a nasal discharge, sneezing and sometimes diarrhoea.

Diagnosis
Diagnosis is made by a laboratory examination of the cat's faeces to detect lungworm eggs or larvae. Sometimes a procedure termed a 'tracheal wash' is performed. In this test, a small amount of fluid is injected directly into the cat's windpipe (the trachea), sucked out again, then examined for lungworm eggs or larvae.

Treatment
Drugs used include levamisole and fenbendazole. These should be used under veterinary supervision as they can be toxic, so correct dose rates are important.

Lung fluke

Lung fluke is an infestation seen in some parts of the USA and South Africa. It is caused by *paragonimus* spp.

Infection occurs when the cat eats raw crabs or crayfish. The severity depends on the number of fluke injected. The main sign is a cough. The cat might bring up a rust-coloured (bloody) sputum. More serious damage occurs if the brain and spinal cord are invaded. The signs depend on what area of the barin is affected, but could include a head tilt or convulsions and fits.

Diagnosis

Microscopic examination of the cat sputum or faeces will reveal characteristic fluke eggs.

Prevention

Do not feed the cat raw crabs or shellfish.

Pleurisy

Pleurisy is also called pleuritis and pyothorax. The lungs are coated with a thin membrane called the pleura, which also coats the chest wall. If the pluera becomes inflamed, due perhaps to infection by bacteria virus, fungi or parasites, or due to an effusive tumour, it produces an exudate that gradually builds up in the chest cavity, pushing the lungs away from the chest wall and therefore making

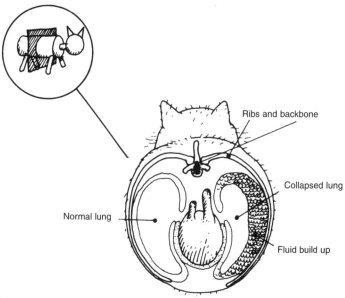

Ribs and backbone

Collapsed lung

Normal lung

Fluid build up

Pleurisy: Fluid builds up between the lung and the chest wall. In pneumonia, the congestion is within the lung itself

breathing difficult and painful. In many cases, the condition is far advanced before the cat shows obvious signs of distress. By this stage, treatment is difficult and often unsuccessful.

Infection can gain entry in a variety of ways. The most common is probably when lung tissue is ruptured, for example due to a kick or car accident. Air breathed into the lungs is usually contaminated by dust and other debris, including fungal spores or bacteria. The lungs are adapted to cope with these contaminants, but the pleura is not. Agents that would be innocuous in the lungs can be responsible for severe infections in the pleural cavity.

Other possible routes of infection include penetrating chest wounds, such as by a broken rib, or bite wounds, or by extensions from lung infections. Some viruses have a specific affinity for the pleura and, once present in the bloodstream, will quickly establish themselves and start growing in the pleura.

Bronchitis

The bronchi are the airways of the lungs. Air comes down the trachea, which then branches out into smaller and smaller passageways taking air deep into the lung tissue. When the bronchi become inflamed, due to infection by virus or bacteria, or inhalation or irritant gases, smoke or dust, allergic reactions, or invasion by parasites, this condition is termed bronchitis.

The primary sign of bronchitis is a harsh cough. It can vary in nature, and can be hard, dry, spasmodic and/or painful.

Treatment
The treatment varies with the cause and severity of the condition. The cause should be eliminated if possible, for example, if the cat is being exposed to excessive fumes or dust.
- Antibiotics are often indicated. Even if bacteria did not start the condition, they will commonly invade once the bronchi are damaged.
- Mucolytics: these are agents that break down the thick, tenacious mucus into a more fluid form that can be dislodged from the bronchi and eliminated from the lungs.
- Bronchodilators: the bronchi have a muscular component. This muscle can contract to narrow the passage through the bronchi. When the

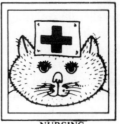

NURSING

bronchi are inflamed there is usually some narrowing of the airways. Bronchodilators are drugs that can reverse this tendency, opening the airways and allowing easier breathing and more efficient expectoration of discharges.

- Humidifying the atmosphere or the use of inhalation agents can help (see chapter 2, 'First Aid').
- Good nursing: improving the cat's general condition can stimulate the cat's own defences. Vitamin supplements do seem to help, especially vitamin A.

In troublesome cases your vet might use cough suppressants or corticosteroids to reduce the inflammation and the severity of the cough.

Treatment of long-standing (chronic) cases of bronchitis can be unrewarding, especially if they have been present since kittenhood.

Bronchial asthma

Bronchial asthma is a condition in which there is a spasm of the smooth muscle of the bronchi. This results in a substantial narrowing of the air passages through the lungs. The cat consequently has increased difficulty breathing. Affected cats make a distinctive wheezing noise. Cats are not as liable to develop asthma as are humans. Siamese are more commonly affected than other breeds.

During severe bouts of asthma the cat might wheeze and cough, gasping for breath. It will be reluctant to move and might sit or lie in one spot with elbows out, breathing laboriously, perhaps even mouth breathing.

Treatment

Treatment includes the use of corticosteroids in injection, tablet or syrup form to control the bronchial spasm. Bronchodilators might also be prescribed.

Prevention

Bronchial asthma is not completely understood. The causes include an allergic reaction to agents (allergens), such as pollen or house dust. If the cat's attacks are seasonal only, then it is likely that some agent such as pollen is responsible. Short courses of corticosteroids during this season might be the best solution. Unfortunately, many cats are afflicted throughout the year. Corticosteroids are by far the most effective treatment. Side effects are minimal in cats, and are far less than in humans.

If you can reduce the cat's exposure to the allergen, this will help. Keep it inside when the pollen counts are high. Avoid exposure to cigarette smoke. You could try electronic air purifiers or ionisers—they have worked dramatically in some cases but failed dismally in others. Naturopathic treatment is also worth consideration.

17 BONES AND JOINTS

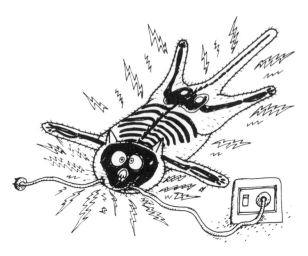

ARTHRITIS

A joint is a flexible connection between two bones. Its purpose is to allow movement. Some joints are relatively simple and permit only a limited range of movement. Others, such as the hip or the jaw, are quite complex and are designed to enable the two bones to move in several directions.

Arthritis means inflammation within a joint. This condition usually results in pain and a degree of lameness. Arthritis is not particularly common in cats, especially when compared with its incidence in humans. For all its apparent familiarity to us, the condition is often poorly understood by cat owners. One particularly common misconception is that arthritis and rheumatism are the same thing. (Rheumatism is a specific type of arthritis.) An understanding of what arthritis is, how it develops, and what you can do about it will help you to cope with an arthritic cat.

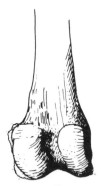
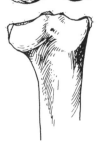

Arthritic changes within the knee joint. Some surfaces wear. Bony spurs and prominences can develop

Signs

The severity of the signs varies with the amount of damage done to the joint and rate at which damage occurs. Signs could include:

- Hot, swollen joint.
- Pain: cat might limp or even refuse to bear weight on the joint.
- Stiffness, lameness. Cat might be slow or reluctant to stand up after rest.
- A general loss or reduction of normal free function.

Treatment

The treatment depends to some extent on the cause of the arthritis. The aim is to minimise further damage and to relieve the pain and inflammation.

When bacterial infection is the cause antibiotics are used, but it is difficult to get antibiotics into the joint and therefore to the site of infection. This is because everything that gets into the joint is filtered, purified and modified first. There is no blood within the joint. Instead, there is joint fluid, which is responsible for lubrication and nutrition. Because the joint is 'protected' from antibiotics, infections within a joint can flourish. Although there are ways of overcoming this problem, it is nevertheless difficult to eliminate an infection without surgical intervention, once it has invaded a joint.

The treatment of arthritis involves controlling the inflammation thus reducing the pain, plus stabilising the joint if possible. This might involve repair of loose or broken ligaments. Reduction of any excess weight will help.

There is a range of drugs that can be used. Aspirin is quite effective, but cats have difficulty in excreting it. If you use aspirin, you should not repeat the dose for at least two days. Better to leave the choice and dose rates of drugs to your vet.

BROKEN BONES

A broken bone is the same as a fractured bone. The terms are synonymous. There are many different types of fractures, and they are classified according to their severity, the number of breaks, the degree of displacement and so on. The main types are as follows:

- Greenstick fracture: the bone is incompletely broken. There is no displacement. This type of fracture usually occurs in young cats when the bones are still relatively flexible.
- Simple fracture: the bone is completely broken and there is some separation between the ends, but the skin is not broken.
- Compound fracture: some bone penetrates the skin. Infection is potentially a problem.

Signs
Some or all of the following are signs of broken bones:
- Loss of function. The cat will not bear weight on a fractured limb. (A fracture of the pelvis might not result in total loss of function.)
- Pain, especially at fracture site.
- Swelling, due to bleeding and bruising. (This can be difficult to see, and the cat will resent your probing.)
- Unnatural degree of movement. For example, the lower part of a limb might swing freely, or the end of the tail drag along. The limb might appear shorter or abnormally twisted.

If you are in doubt, it is useful to compare the damaged part with the same part on the other side of the body.

First aid
- Be careful. The cat might resent handling. (Read chapter 2, 'First Aid'.)

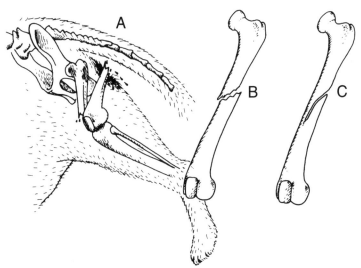

A. Compound fracture (skin broken). B. Simple fracture. C. Greenstick fracture

- Do not attempt to apply a splint.
- In transporting the cat, move slowly to minimise movement of the injured part. Let the damaged limb hang free.

Treatment

To mend, a bone must be set back in the correct position and then be held there rigidly for many weeks.

Plaster casts have never been particularly satisfactory in cats because they are heavy and the cat often resents the encumbrance. Improved synthetic casting materials are lighter, stronger and water repellent. They are much less uncomfortable for the cat.

'Internal fixation' involves the use of surgical pins, plates, screws and wire. Internal fixation is used commonly now. A major advantage of this method is that it allows some use of a limb while repair occurs. Healing is faster, and there is usually not as much muscle wasting. The increasing sophistication of veterinary surgery now allows the successful treatment of most fractures with minimum discomfort and a rapid return to normal use.

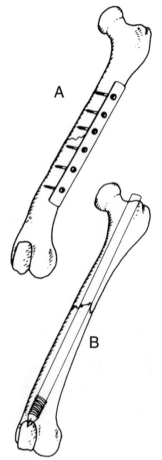

(A) Repair of fractured femur with a stainless steel bone plate and screws; (B) Repair using a steel bone pin

SOME COMMON FRACTURES

Broken jaw

Cats falling from a height sometimes smack the lower jaw hard against the ground. The most common injury is to split the jawbone, although the shafts are sometimes also broken.

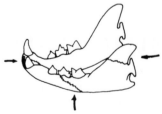

Common sites of jaw fractures

Broken tail

Because the nerves run through the tail, injuries can be serious. If there is much displacement of the broken ends there is likely to be nerve damage, resulting in a paralysed tail that might need to be amputated.

Fractured pelvis

Fractures of the pelvis are among the most common seen in veterinary practice. Most result from car accidents. The treatment depends on how much displacement has occurred. Many do not need any internal or external fixation. By simply putting the cat into a small cage and therefore forcing it to rest, the pelvis will usually heal quickly and with little apparent discomfort to the cat. The muscles of the pelvis go into 'spasm' and can effectively hold the fracture immobile while it heals—providing that the cat does not jump or move too much. Most cats seem perfectly content to sit in a cage for the 10–14 days necessary.

If there is a lot of displacement, your vet might need to realign the bones and perhaps use internal fixation to keep them aligned.

DISLOCATIONS

A dislocation occurs when a bone is displaced from its normal position within a joint. This usually requires considerable force. The joint capsule is simultaneously painfully stretched, and there is usually also some damage to joint ligaments and other supporting tissues.

The signs are similar to a fracture, and an X-ray might be needed to differentiate between them. The most commonly affected joint is the hip.

Dislocated bones are usually manipulated back into their correct position while the cat is deeply anaesthetised. The problem then is to prevent the damaged and unstable joint from dislocating again. Sometimes the limb is bandaged in position, or perhaps surgery may be required to help stabilise the joint. 'Cage rest' is usually recommended for a few days.

SLIPPING KNEECAP

A congenital defect in the knee joint of some cats allows the kneecap to slip out of its correct position (called luxating patella). (The kneecap should lie in a groove at the end of the thigh bone.) This condition is common in some strains of the Devon Rex breed. Surgical repair is possible, but affected cats should not be used for breeding.

SPRAINS

Sprains are injuries to the joints, usually due to overstretching or rupture of the joint capsule or ligaments. The main signs are pain, swelling and lameness. It can be difficult to distinguish between a sprain, a fracture, a dislocation or an acute infection of the joint (due, for example, to a bite) without a careful examination and perhaps an X-ray.

Treatment involves rest. Cats resent the application of ice-packs, which are used routinely in human sprains, and you must not rub on ligaments or ointments designed for human use. These topical ointments can cause pain and skin damage, and the cat will try to lick them off, causing salivation, distress and perhaps vomiting.

In most cases the cat will restrict the activity itself, but try to avoid situations in which the cat has to jump down from a height. If your cat is a climber it might be necessary to confine it in a cage for 1–2 weeks.

When to call the vet

If the cat has a simple sprain, home treatment is usually satisfactory. However, because it is difficult to distinguish between a sprain and, say, a bite wound or a dislocation, you should seek veterinary advice, especially if:

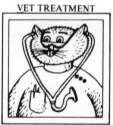

VET TREATMENT

URGENT

- Cat is listless, won't eat.
- Cat is in considerable pain.
- Injury deteriorates—especially if the swelling is increasing.
- Injury fails to respond to treatment.

BONE TUMOURS

A bone tumour is a serious condition, recognised by a sudden onset of lameness that progresses to a painful swelling, usually near a joint. The most common site is in the long bones of the legs. It is hard to differentiate between a bone tumour and a fracture.

The most common tumour is an osteosarcoma, which is a highly malignant tumour. Secondary tumours are liable to spread quickly, especially to the lungs—often before a diagnosis is even made.

At present, the only treatment that gives the cat any chance is amputation of the affected limb. It is only performed if X-rays of the lungs show that secondary tumours have not already established themselves there. Even so, the chances of the cat living for even a further six months are poor.

18 NERVES

Nerves form the communicating link between all parts of the body. They possess unique properties, but suffer from one significant disability: they are unable to heal once they have been badly damaged. If your cat suffers nerve damage your main aim is to minimise further damage.

SPINAL INJURY

VET TREATMENT

URGENT

Spinal injury is serious because an unbroken, unimpaired link between the brain and the rest of the body is fundamental to good health. The network of nerves relays information from every part of the body. Vast amounts of data are transmitted to the brain, but the nerves are essential for the execution of all voluntary, and many involuntary, body functions.

The spinal cord is composed of innumerable individual nerves running together through the spinal canal, protected and supported by the vertebrae. Any damage to the spinal cord has grave repercussions further afield in the body. If communication between the brain and a limb or an organ is lost, all conscious and most unconscious control is also lost. If the nerves are badly damaged, this loss of control could be permanent.

If the spinal cord is cut or crushed in the neck, the cat will die. Control of the diaphragm is lost, and therefore the cat cannot

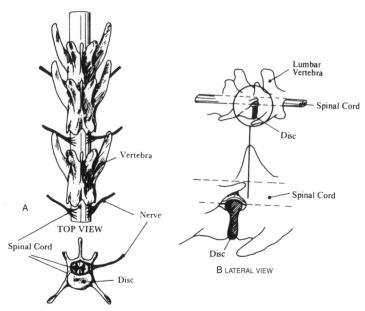

(A) A vertebra has been slid back to show how the nerves branch off the main spinal cord; (B) Disc disease: The nucleus of the intervertebral disc has ruptured and is compressing the spinal cord against the roof of the spinal canal

breathe. In general, the closer to the cat's brain that spinal damage occurs, the worse is the outlook for the cat's future.

Causes

The causes of spinal injury include trauma, disc disease, infectious disease, tumours, and conditions that cause changes in the bones of the spine.

Trauma is the most common cause of spinal injury. It requires violent physical force to overcome the protective defences of the vertebrae, but serious damage could result from a motor car accident, a kick, fall from a height, or a gunshot wound or something similar.

Degeneration or disease of the intervertebral discs (see diagram) can result in the protrusion of matter from the disc's nucleus into the spinal canal, causing pain, paresis (weakness or reduced function), or paralysis.

Some infectious agents have a particular affinity with nerve tissue, notably the rabies virus. Others occasionally involve nerves, for example, feline infectious peritonitis, toxoplasmosis, and cryptococcosis.

The most common tumour involving the spinal cord is lymphosarcoma (also called lymphoma). It is a malignant tumour and is often associated with infection by the feline leukemia virus or the feline immunodeficiency virus (see chapter 9, 'Infectious diseases').

Conditions that cause changes in the bones of the spine, or remodelling of them, can result in increased pressure on the spinal cord. These conditions include vitamin A and/or D excesses and calcium deficiencies or excesses.

Signs

Signs of spinal injury could include pain, paralysis, and loss of sensation. The degree of damage inflicted and the location of the injury are critical factors in determining the severity of the signs.

In severe injury there is a loss of all sensation, including pain, beyond the injured area. In milder injuries, sensitivity to pain could be increased. In mild injury there might only be weakness or reduced function (paresis) rather than paralysis, i.e. a total loss of function.

Loss of sensation is often the first sign of degenerative nerve disease. Humans can complain to their physician of a tingling sensation or numbness, but in the cat you can only observe the effects of this loss of sensation. Because the cat lacks feeling or sensation in an area, it could inadvertently damage it. For example, a damaged tail might become fouled with urine. In cleaning the tail, the cat might damage the skin, causing inflammation and ulceration because it lacks the sensitivity to prevent its rough tongue from rasping the skin.

Other possible signs of spinal injury include stiff forelegs; dribbling urine, or involuntary retention of urine; loss of normal bowel control—diarrhoea or constipation; and abnormal posture and movements.

First aid

Your main task is to avoid further damage to the nerves. Once the vertebral column has been damaged it might no longer protect the spinal cord efficiently. Careless handling could result in further destruction of irreplaceable nerve cells.

- Find a board or a box with a firm bottom where the cat can lie flat without having to curl up. If the surface is smooth it is preferable to cover it with a blanket so that the injured cat does not slip around.
- Put the cat on to the board or into the box. This can be difficult. Take care. If possible, slide it on to the blanket, then— supporting it with the flat of both hands so that the spine does not sag—put the whole bundle on to the flat, firm supporting surface of the box or board.

If the cat struggles, or is uncooperative or is trying to bite or scratch, first cover it with a large towel or blanket. Pack the material firmly around it, enveloping the entire body. Then remove the whole lot—blanket, cat, and all—into a box, doing your best to avoid bending the cat's spine.

- Get to a vet as soon as possible. Spinal injury is too serious for home treatment. When travelling, go slowly and smoothly. You won't help the injury by bouncing the patient around in a frantic dash to get to the vet.

Treatment should be commenced as soon as possible after the injury has occurred, and preferably within an hour. If treatment is commenced more than 24 hours after serious injury, then the chances of achieving a successful outcome are greatly reduced.

Veterinary treatment

Treatment of acute injuries could include treatment to reduce inflammation or swelling in and around the spinal cord and to control further bleeding. The damaged area might have to be immobilised. In some cases, surgical treatment is indicated to relieve pressure on the injured cord. Such surgery must be undertaken as soon after the injury as possible, and it should preferably be performed by a very experienced surgeon.

Treatment of chronic spinal conditions, which have resulted in a gradual onset of signs, is less urgent. The vet has time to assess the patient carefully before deciding on the most satisfactory course of treatment.

DISC DISEASE

Disc disease (disease of the intervertebral disc) is not particularly common in cats. This is in contrast to the situation in dogs and humans, where problems due to degeneration or rupture of the spinal discs are frequently encountered.

When feline disease occurs, it is usually the result of direct physical trauma, such as a motor car accident, although chronic deterioration with age does occur. Disc disease is most likely to occur in cats older than 15 years. The discs between the neck vertebrae are the ones most commonly affected. Sometimes the nucleus of the disc deteriorates, ruptures and presses on the spinal cord yet causes no apparent discomfort. This is possible only if the protrusion occurs very gradually. It is not uncommon to find, during routine autopsy, that an aged cat has protrusion of several spinal discs, although it had never shown clinical signs while alive.

If a disc protrudes as the result of trauma, sudden pressure may be applied to the spinal cord. This is usually aggravated by inflammation as the material in the disc's nucleus is very irritant. The cat will probably be in considerable pain, and there might be weakness or paralysis.

POISONS

Cats are less likely to be poisoned than dogs, but could inadvertently ingest poisons that cause nerve damage. The following is a list of some of the more common poisons that cause nervous signs:

- Ethylene glycol (anti-freeze).
- Aspirin.
- Benzoic acid.
- Chlorinated hydrocarbons (insecticides).
- Lead.
- Mercury.
- Metaldehyde (snail bait).
- Organophosphates (snail bait and other pesticides).
- Streptomycin (an antibiotic).

SEIZURES

There is constant electrical activity in the brain, even during sleep and rest. The brain controls the entire body via messages transmitted as electrical impulses through the nerves. A seizure or fit is caused by a violent burst of electrical activity within the brain, similar to the surging discharge of energy seen as lightning during thunderstorms.

If the causative agent is gradually producing more pressure or irritation, as would occur if a tumour is growing within the brain, the fits will become more frequent and more severe. In other cases, the body might be able to excrete the irritant, or contain it in some way, and the fits could cease altogether. This is usually the case in infections or poisonings that have been successfully treated; there is often no permanent damage, assuming treatment is commenced promptly.

Epilepsy

Epilepsy is characterised by a recurring pattern of seizures one after the other, then an interval of days or weeks before the next series. In most other species, such as dogs, there is just a single fit, rather than a series. Epileptic attacks might start in the young cat around puberty, or they might begin some weeks or months after a blow to the head, such as could have been inflicted in a car accident. This sort of seizure is due to scar tissue that gradually contracts to produce a focal source of irritation to the brain. Many epileptic attacks are classified as 'idiopathic', which means 'of unknown cause'.

Causes

Fits or seizures are generally precipitated by something causing localised pressure, inflammation or irritation in the brain. Some of the more common causes include:

- Head injury: bleeding can result from pressure on the brain, or scars might gradually form that eventually—weeks or even months later—produce a focus of pressure on the brain.
- Toxic chemicals, especially lead, also insecticides, anti-freeze and others.
- Infectious agents, especially toxoplasmosis, feline infectious peritonitis and cryptococcosis, but others could be involved.
- Tumours: lymphosarcoma following feline leukaemia virus infection is the most common.
- Thiamine deficiency: due to a diet rich in raw fish, or meat products with suphur dioxide added as a preservative.

Other conditions, when seizures or fits can be a major presenting sign, include liver disease, kidney failure, low blood sugar (hypoglycaemia), and milk fever.

Signs

- Sudden onset of violent, uncontrolled muscle spasms.
- Tremor.
- Collapse.
- Loss of consciousness (from transient to prolonged).
- Paddling movements of the legs.
- Stiffness or rigidity of the body.
- Involuntary salivation.
- 'Rage reaction': the cat growls and hisses, might not be aware of its surroundings, and does not react to normal stimulations, such as calling its name.

Most fits or seizures last only a few seconds but might last several minutes. It always seems much longer at the time. Cats can have several convulsions in one day, then a period of apparent normal health, followed by another series.

Recovery from fits is usually spontaneous. Owners frequently erroneously believe that something they have done has produced the recovery, for example, stroking the cat, or throwing cold water over it. In fact, there is virtually nothing you can do for the cat while it is in the grip of a convulsion. You should not interfere unless you have to as there is a real danger of being hurt. A fit that is continuous and does not spontaneously cease is termed *status epilepticus*. It requires urgent veterinary attention.

On recovery, the cat will be quiet and appear dazed or confused. many will go away and hide in a dark, quiet place. Some temporarily become quite unpredictable, even vicious. Others crave affection, comfort and soothing.

Treatment

Treatment can be rewarding. Daily tablets will be necessary, plus a close liaison with your vet. It takes time to find the most suitable dose rates and the most effective drugs. Once the fits have been controlled successfully, the cat can usually live a normal life.

Action

- Most fits end spontaneously, so—stand back. Leave the cat where it is unless it is in danger (such as on a road or near an open fire). The cat is unlikely to die during a fit, unless it is very prolonged. If you *must* move a convulsing cat, first throw a large towel or blanket over it, completely enveloping it. Then move the whole bundle to a safer area.
- *Don't* put your finger into the cat's mouth. You will be bitten if you do. Cats virtually never swallow their tongue, so there is usually no necessity to try to open the mouth.
- Leave the cat until the convulsion has ended. *Do not* attempt to stroke, hold or cuddle the cat either during or immediately after an episode.
- Approach with caution. The cat will be unpredictable and could uncharacteristically bite or scratch through fear or confusion. Try to get it to a quiet, dark room. Once it has sufficiently recovered, transport it to the vet for examination.

RADIAL NERVE PARALYSIS

Radial nerve paralysis is the most common 'single' nerve condition. We have probably all experienced mild episodes of radial nerve paralysis. If you fall asleep across your arm you might inadvertently put pressure on the radial nerve where it runs around your elbow. On awakening, you might have a temporary loss of feeling and strength in the arm. After a few minutes, and a period of 'pins and needles', the arm goes back to normal.

The radial nerve is more liable to damage than most because it runs close to the surface and lies on top of a bone, where it could be crushed. If hit hard enough, the damage can be serious—even permanent.

Radial nerve (foreleg) paralysis

The most common cause of radial nerve paralysis in cats is a car accident, but it could also be damaged in a fight, or if the foreleg is caught in a fence, a trap or something similar.

Signs
- Affected foreleg cannot bear weight.
- Leg folds up when the cat attempts to stand on it, or the foot might be dragged along the ground as the cat walks.
- A lack of sensation on the front of the foot over the top of the toes. Sores or ulcers might develop on the feet where they are dragged over the ground.

Treatment
The outlook depends on how badly the nerve has been damaged. If the nerve is only bruised, treatment to reduce inflammation and swelling will prevent increased pressure on the nerve and therefore further damage. In many instances, recovery is spontaneous. Most cases improve or even recover completely within 24 hours. Others take up to several weeks. If the nerve is severely damaged, it will not heal. In this case, treatment depends on how the cat copes with the affliction

Amputation of the affected limb could become necessary, especially if there has been other damage such as skin loss or multiple fractures. It could also be indicated if the cat is self-traumatising the insensitive skin by licking or damaging it as the leg drags over the ground.

OTHER COMMON NERVE INJURIES

Two other fairly common nerve injuries that result in significant loss of function are:

1. Sciatic nerve damage in the hindleg (most likely as a complication of a fractured femur).

2. Damage to the brachial plexus, which is a group of nerves lying between the foreleg and the body wall. The entire group of nerves is sometimes torn when the leg is forcibly pulled away from the body wall. Again, usually a car accident is responsible.

In the situation where much of the nervous control is lost, the cat cannot hold the leg up out of trouble so the limb impedes walking and will probably become ulcerated and infected. Unfortunately you have only two options: either have the limb amputated or have your cat humanely euthanised.

VITAMIN A POISONING

Vitamin A is an essential element in the cat's diet. However, it can be taken in excess and accumulate to toxic levels. This usually occurs in cats fed large amounts of liver, but could result from over-supplementation of cod liver and vitamin preparations.

Signs
- Stiff neck. Usually first noticed because the cat cannot groom itself properly.
- Foreleg lameness. Usually intermittent at first.
- Pain in legs and body.
- Abnormal gait and posture.

These signs occur because vitamin A causes minerals to be laid down in the ligaments of the spine. The normally elastic ligaments become hard and inflexible. Excessive bone is also laid down in the neck vertebrae and back vertebrae. Initially this causes pain when the cat moves, and eventually produces rigidity of the spine so the cat cannot bend its neck or get much movement of the normally flexible spine.

If this condition is diagnosed early, the excessive mineralisation of ligaments and abnormal bone formation could gradually resolve. The diet must be corrected and drugs such as cortico-steroids might be needed to help relieve the pain and inflammation and to speed recovery. Advanced cases might be incurable.

THE ALL-MEAT DIET

Cats that are fed a predominantly or exclusively meat diet develop an imbalance of minerals, calcium and phosphorus. As meat is also deficient in other nutrients such as iodine, magnesium and several vitamins, the clinical picture could be clouded by other deficiency conditions, but basically this condition results in poor bone structure and is most common in young, growing kittens. Their bones have thin shafts, the joints swell, and the cat is liable to joint pain. The bones are easily fractured. In advanced cases the bone might even collapse in what is termed a 'folding fracture'.

Signs

- Increasing irritability (due to pain).
- Lameness: often a 'shifting' lameness where first one leg then another is favoured. In fact all the legs are involved, but one is usually more sore than the others.
- Deformities of legs: usually bowing of the forelegs and swollen, mushrooming joints.
- Fractures.
- Constipation, as a result of deformity of spine or pelvis.

Treatment

Improve the cat's diet to a balanced one and give a calcium supplement for a few weeks. The best calcium sources are calcium carbonate (chalk), calcium gluconate or calcium lactate. Dose: 1 teaspoon or 1 tablet per 5 kg body weight per day. *Do not* use DCP (di-calcium phosphate). An improvement is usually seen in kittens within a week or two.

Owners faced with a diagnosis of this condition quite often say 'But I give him milk. Isn't that a good source of calcium?' The answer is *yes*, it is, but although it can help prevent the condition from developing, it is unsuitable as a treatment, because it lacks the required balance of calcium to phosphorus. A cat would have to drink 600 ml (1 pint) of milk daily to meet its calcium requirement!

THIAMINE DEFICIENCY

Thiamine deficiency is also called Chastek's paralysis. Thiamine is a vitamin, one of the B group. It is one of the few vitamins that the cat cannot produce itself. It must therefore be supplied in the diet. Fortunately, many of the cat's natural foods such as liver and kidney are rich in thiamine. Other sources include whole grain and green vegetables. Actual dietary deficiencies are not common. The usual cause of thiamine deficiency is excessive destruction of thiamine by a substance called thiaminase, which is found in raw fish. Cats fed large amounts of raw fish will develop Chastek's paralysis.

Overcooking food, or the use of preservatives such as sulphur dioxide, can also destroy thiamine. Some commercial foods are marginally deficient in thiamine. Sometimes stress (such as illness, pregnancy or an emotional upset) can precipitate the condition.

Signs

- Loss of weight.
- Lack of appetite.

- Irritability.
- Progressive weakness.
- Vomiting.
- Eventually convulsions, loss of balance. Affected cats tend to walk with their head down and claws extended.

Treatment

Supplement the diet with thiamine, and stop feeding raw fish. If nervous signs have started, an injection of thiamine will rapidly produce an improvement in the cat, usually within a day.

Even though commercial food manufacturers are aware of the problems, cases of thiamine deficiency still occur in some cats that have been fed one particular brand. Cats are unlikely to develop this problem if they are fed a variety of commercial products.

In severe cases there might be irreversible brain damage. These cats should be euthanised.

STROKE

A 'stroke' (or vascular accident) is the term for the syndrome that occurs following bleeding on the brain or due to a blood clot forming in the brain, resulting in a localised area of brain damage. Strokes are not common in cats. They are most likely to occur in cats more than 10 years old.

Signs

The signs of a stroke are due to pressure on the brain or to the effects of oxygen starvation to a discrete area. The signs depend on which particular part of the brain is affected. The sudden onset of one or more of the following signs could indicate a 'stroke'.

- Loss of consciousness.
- Loss of function of one side of the body. It could involve only the face, or could be more extensive and involve one or both limbs on the same side of the body.
- Severe mental depression: a state of semi-stupor.
- Dilated pupil or pupils.
- Loss of balance, pacing and circling in one direction (consistently to the left or consistently to the right).
- Dramatic or sudden change in behaviour.

Treatment

Treatment depends on the severity and extent of brain damage. Most cats will spontaneously recover from a slight stroke with time, good nursing, and perhaps some drug treatment from your vet. There could be residual problems, such as partial blindness, behavioural changes or recurring fits (epilepsy).

NURSING

TICK PARALYSIS

Some ticks carry a nerve toxin in their salivary glands. The most dangerous of them are the Ixodes species, which is common on the east coast of Australia, and *Dermacentor andersoni*, which is found in some southern states of the USA. Cats are not as susceptible to the effects of tick toxin as other animals, notably dogs. Some cats living in tick country gradually acquire an immunity or resistance to the toxin.

Signs
- A change in the cat's miaow.
- Coughing and gagging.

Gradually, other signs develop:
- Progressive weakness then paralysis of the limbs, starting with the tail and hindquarters, ascending towards the head.
- Breathing becomes laboured.
- Eventually death from respiratory failure.

Treatment

Once signs have started, treatment becomes urgent, although you have at least 24 hours before the cat would die (less if there are several ticks). First remove the tick, then go straight to a vet if any signs of weakness or paralysis is developing. A specific antidote (anti-tick serum) is available.

Removing ticks

Place an inverted bottle of alcohol or methylated spirits over the tick. It will soon release and drop off. Or paint the tick with nail polish remover (acetone). Do not squeeze the tick. The toxin is contained in the tick's salivary glands, and by squeezing you could inject more poison into the cat. For the same reason you must be sure to get the head out. Don't just break off the body.

19 CANCER

Few words evoke such sinister connotations as cancer. While a diagnosis of cancer causes some dismay, the situation is by no means hopeless. Many cancers are treatable, especially if recognised and treated early.

A cancer is a growth that is beyond the body's control. Most of the body's cells are capable of multiplying, but when they multiply it is to replace or repair damaged or worn-out cells, or as a normal part of growth. It is when the body loses the ability to limit or constrain the multiplication of cells that a tumour develops.

TYPES OF GROWTHS

A *tumour* is defined as any swelling or lump. A tumour can be any group of cells growing beyond the control of the host's body. Tumours may be benign or malignant. Many tumours do not fit neatly into one category or the other. Others can gradually change their nature from benign to malignant. A definite diagnosis of tumour type is not always possible. A benign tumour is not a great threat to your cat's life. These tumours do not eat into surrounding tissue. They expand and grow from within, somewhat like a balloon being slowly blown up. A malignant tumour is also called a cancer. This tumour grows out from its borders, invading and destroying surrounding tissues. Sometimes cancerous cells break away from the parent tumour and take root some distance away, growing a 'secondary' tumour. Common sites for secondary tumour growth include the lungs, liver and abdominal cavity.

Table 5 will make the distinction between benign and malignant clearer.

Table 5: Characteristics of tumours

Characteristic	Benign	Malignant
Rate of growth	Slow	Usually rapid
Shape	Usually regular—round or oval, with readily defined borders	Irregular. Often difficult to tell exactly where the limits of growth are
Pain	Usually does not concern the cat. Depends on the position of the tumour	Often inflamed. Possible swelling, pain and discharge. Cat is usually concerned
Do they invade surrounding tissue	No	Yes
Do they spread locally or to other organs?	No	Sometimes

According to the results of one survey, every year an average of two in every 1000 cats develop a tumour. In the cat, an unusually high percentage of all tumours are malignant—around 80%. This is much higher than for dogs or humans.

Causes
The causes are largely unknown, although a small percentage of cancers in cats is produced by the feline leukaemia virus.

Treatment
The main weapons against cancer are surgical removal of a tumour and treatment of the mass with drugs, radiation or other therapies. Your vet will judge each case on its merits and advise accordingly. It is not always possible to know whether a tumour is malignant or benign until a pathologist has examined a portion of it microscopically. If your cat has to be anaesthetised to obtain a biopsy, many vets will opt to remove the entire growth (if possible) rather than just take out a piece of it.

The position if the tumour must also be considered. A tumour that is growing, for example, on an eyelid or the lip will cause irritation or pain. If so, it should be removed even if it is thought to be benign.

Surgery

Because of the invasive nature of their growth, it is often difficult to determine the precise borders of a cancer. The surgeon will usually try to take out not only the tumour but also an area of apparently healthy tissue surrounding the tumour. The aim is also to remove any unseen cancer cells that might by infiltrating locally and might otherwise grow to replace the primary tumour. It is not always possible to remove all of the potentially involved tissue. For example, the tumour might be on the skin of the face, or on an eyelid. Too much loss of tissue from these areas could be disfiguring, or perhaps the surgeon would be unable to close the resultant wound.

Drugs

Treatment of cancer by drugs is called chemotherapy. Many drugs and chemicals known to be able to kill cancer are available. They act on rapidly dividing cells in the body, which includes healthy cells as well as cancerous ones. Careful monitoring using blood tests and symptomatic treatment of side effects is necessary. For some cats and some owners the side effects of this treatment make it unacceptable.

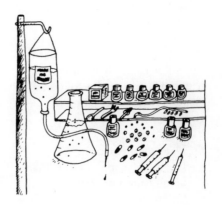

Radiation

The use of X-rays to destroy malignant cells can be very effective. Cancerous cells are more sensitive to X-rays than normal cells. Sophisticated machines are required that can focus the X-rays precisely into the tumour. Some tumours, especially skin tumours, can be effectively treated this way, but the apparatus is not widely available due to its expense.

Radioactive implants can be used. There are small 'needles' of radioactive material that are inserted into the tumour mass. They emit intense radiation over a very short distance and are capable of destroying some tumours without affecting surrounding healthy tissues.

Electromagnetic pulse therapy and laser beam therapy are two other forms of treatment that show promise, but are yet to be fully developed.

Outlook

The most common complication to arise in the treatment of malignant tumours is when the tumour cells have already spread to other parts of the cat's body. There is little point in removing the primary tumour if there are multiple secondary tumours growing elsewhere. If a malignant tumour is removed before it has had time to spread, the cat should recover to normal health.

SKIN TUMOURS

The two most common skin tumours of cats are the squamous cell carcinoma and the basal cell carcinoma. Both are malignant. Fortunately, owners often detect early enough for treatment to be successful.

Any new lump or growth that appears in your cat's skin should be carefully examined. If it exhibits any of the following characteristics it should be checked by your vet:

- Rapid growth.
- Dark pigmentation.
- Irregular shape (rather than being round or oval).
- Open, ulcerated or raw surface.
- Is causing discomfort.

Squamous cell carcinoma is more common in white or unpigmented skin on ear tips, nose and eyelids

If a malignant tumour is detected and removed before it has spread to other organs the cat's life might be saved.

Squamous cell carcinoma

Excessive exposure to sunlight is strongly incriminated in the cause of squamous cell carcinoma, although other factors are also involved. The ultraviolet radiation of sunlight is particularly dangerous to unpigmented skin, especially in areas such as the ears, nose and eyelids where there is no hair cover either. For this reason, white cats living in warm climates are at risk if they are allowed to lie in the sun.

The typical sites of squamous cell carcinoma are the ear tips, nose and eyelids. It also occurs on the lips and mouth. It usually appears as a single growth. It is irregular in size and shape, and the surface is usually ulcerated (i.e. open and raw). Eventually it appears to be eroding the skin.

Early in its course, a squamous cell carcinoma can easily be mistaken for a bite or scratch wound.

Basal cell carcinoma

Basal cell carcinomas usually only invade locally and do not commonly spread to other organs such as the lungs. Treatment by wide surgical incision can be curative.

These tumours are most common on the back of the head, neck and withers, but can be found anywhere. They usually occur as a single, rounded and hairless lump with a rubbery consistency. Most of them eventually ulcerate.

MAMMARY TUMOURS

Tumours involving the mammary glands (breasts) comprise about a quarter of all tumours occurring in female cats. They are rare in males or in females who have been spayed when young. Unfortunately, most feline mammary tumours are malignant. The majority of the cats affected are old. Their average age is 11 years.

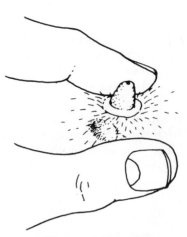

The tumours can be palpated as lumps in the mammary glands. The entire gland can become firm. The skin surface sometimes ulcerates, oozing a blood-stained fluid. They might attach firmly to the body wall, but are usually moveable.

Early detection of mammary tumours gives a better chance of successful treatment

Mammary tumours can be confused with mammary cysts. These cysts are fairly common in older queens and are due to a blockage of the milk ducts. They are firm and seem fluid-filled when touched. They are usually not painful.

Treatment

If the tumour is detected early, your vet might recommend removal of the affected mammary glands and perhaps of the entire chain of glands. An X-ray of the cat's chest might be taken first. If the tumour has already spread to the lungs or other organs, or if the case is far advanced, successful treatment will not be possible.

LYMPHOSARCOMA

A third of all tumours seen in cats are lymphosarcoma, a malignant tumour associated with infection by the feline leukaemia virus (Fe.LV—see chapter 9, 'Infectious diseases'.)

The cat's lymphoid tissue is responsible for the production of antibodies, which give immunity against many bacterial and viral diseases. Lymph tissue includes the tonsils and adenoids and many other lymph nodes or 'glands' spread right throughout the body. Their role is to filter body fluid (or 'lymph') before it is returned to the bloodstream to continue circulating. The thymus and spleen are also lymphoid tissue.

The feline leukaemia virus can induce cancer in this lymphoid tissue. Because lymphoid tissue is so widespread, the sites of tumour formation, and therefore the clinical signs, are very variable. The most common organs to be affected are the intestines, thymus gland (in the neck and chest), kidneys, spleen and brain or spinal cord. Some breeds, notably the Siamese, have a much higher than average incidence of lymphosarcoma.

Treatment
Treatment is not usually recommended. This is for two reasons:
1. The tumour is usually not surgically accessible. There could be many secondary tumours, so detection and removal of all tumours may be impossible.
2. The affected cat is likely to be a source of FeLV infection to other cats.

20 THE OLD CAT

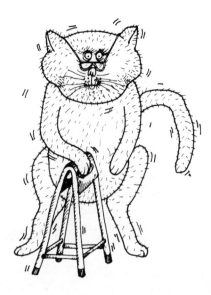

As your cat moves into old age you can help to keep it healthy and comfortable in many ways. For example, some simple additions to its diet will minimise the risk of deficiencies and significantly reduce stresses on vital organs such as the liver and kidney.

Ageing is a gradual process. Warning signs of organ deterioration are usually not dramatic but rather insidious in onset. In humans the heart and arteries are often the first to fail. In cats, the kidneys are their Achilles heel.

The average lifespan of an unneutered male cat living in the wild is less than four years. A domestic cat, neutered, and living in a protected situation will usually live to 12–15 years of age. Many reach 18 or 20. The oldest known cat was Puss from Devon, England, who died the day after his thirty-sixth birthday.

THE AGEING PROCESS

A pessimist once described life as 'a terminal condition'. There is some truth in his view. All of the body's organs must slowly deteriorate and become less efficient. Muscles waste, the colour of the coat changes, the skin loses its elasticity and tone. It is not possible to give a precise age at which a cat is considered 'old'. Individuals vary. Some of the changes that occur in a cat's later life include the following:

- The senses deteriorate. Smell, taste, sight and hearing are all impaired to some degree, although it is rare for a cat to lose one of these senses entirely.
- The skin becomes less elastic, the coat loses its glossy sheen, and the hairs tend to clump together and stick up. Because the cat is less inclined to groom, discharges can build up around the eyes, ears and anus.
- Muscle tone deteriorates. This includes not only the skeletal muscles of the limbs and trunk but also the muscles within the bowel wall and others such as the bladder sphincter. The bowel might become less effective in propelling food through the digestive tract, which results in the cat becoming liable to bouts of constipation and/or diarrhoea. If the muscle tone of the bladder sphincter is reduced, the cat will start to dribble urine. If the anal sphincter is affected it will pass a lot of foul gas or occasionally inadvertently pass faeces.
- The liver and pancreas gradually deteriorate. In some old cats, one of these organs might eventually fail to produce enough digestive enzymes to digest food adequately. The cat usually continues to eat well but loses weight. The faeces of these cats are usually loose or ill-formed, yellow or greasy.
- Decrease in energy levels and agility. The old cat is content to spend most of its day sleeping.
- Teeth might be lost. This is usually due to gum disease, but is also partly due to loosening of the teeth in their sockets as the jaw bones become less flexible and more chalky.
- Resistance to disease decreases. Old cats are more susceptible to diseases such as cat flu. When they are sick they deteriorate faster, having less strength and stamina than young cats. Healing takes longer.
- Resistance to parasites decreases. Cats that have never previously been troubled by fleas can develop heavy burdens. Similarly, internal worm parasites such as hookworm can multiply to infest in numbers that significantly affect the cat's health.
- Old cats are less adaptable to changes such as moving house, a new pet, a new baby or even just a rearrangement of the furniture. A change in diet is often no problem for a young cat but a considerable stress for an old one.
- The old cat is likely to suffer from:
  — Kidney disease.

— Mouth conditions.
— Skin tumours.
— Arthritis.
— Heart disease (rarely).

LOOKING AFTER AN OLD CAT

Some routine measures that can be taken with any older cat can include the following:

- Feed smaller meals, more often. This gives the digestive system a better chance to digest the food effectively, and it evens out the stresses on vital organs such as the kidney and liver.
- Do not feed large amounts of rich red meats such as beef heart. White meats and fish are more easily digested, and have less toxic wastes for the kidney to excrete.
- A multivitamin/mineral supplement is an excellent idea. Cats make most of their own vitamins. As they get older, a supplement of vitamins significantly improves the health of many cats. Perhaps their production has fallen below optimum, or perhaps the requirements of old tissues for vitamins are higher. The levels of various minerals such as copper, zinc and iron can become depleted, so a supplement that provides both vitamins and minerals, and probably also some trace elements, is often successful in rejuvenating an old cat. It is better to use a preparation formulated specifically for cats than to use a human preparation, as feline requirements are significantly different from ours.

- Add a pinch of salt to the daily ration. It will supply sodium and encourages drinking, which keeps the kidney flushing and reduces the incidence of constipation. Do not add more than $\frac{1}{8}$ teaspoon per day, and do not add any if the cat has a heart condition and your vet has advised salt restriction.
- Pamper the cat a little. Make sure the sleeping area is warm and draught-free. You might even allow the cat to sleep near a source of warmth such as water heater or heat bank.

- Constipation is a common problem. If this is the case with your cat, read the relevant section in chapter 14, 'The gut'. Some roughage (such as bran) added to the diet can effectively prevent recurrences. Avoid excessive amounts of dry food and bones. You might occasionally have to give a laxative such as liquid paraffin.
- Groom the cat daily. Regular combing and brushing will keep your cat more comfortable by removing dead hairs that irritate the skin, or which could otherwise be ingested and lead to constipation.
- Clear away any discharges from the eyes. If necessary, clean the ears. Check the anal area for soiled or matted fur.
- Worm the old cat every 6 months. Your vet will supply a suitable preparation.

VETERINARY CHECK-UPS

VET TREATMENT

URGENT

A regular check-up of an old cat can be well worthwhile. Because vets are very familiar with the problems an old cat is liable to encounter, they might be able to pick up subtle warning signs long before you do. Some of the points your vet will pay particular attention to include:

BOOSTER

- Teeth. Gum disease and the formation of tartar or dental calculus is a common cause of discomfort. Early treatment can save teeth, and the cat will certainly be more comfortable without inflamed gums.
- Vaccination. Booster vaccinations are sensible because the old cat's immune system gradually becomes less efficient.
- Parasites. Internal and external parasites can build up to affect an old cat's health significantly.
- Diet. Your vet may discuss possible deficiencies or changes needed.
- A general check might indicate possible problems in organs such as the kidney, liver and lungs. Your vet might want to run some tests to check on possible problems.

SPECIFIC CONDITIONS OF OLD AGE

Kidney disease or deterioration

Warning signs could include:
- Increased thirst.
- Increased appetite (later in the course the appetite might decline or be lost).
- Bad breath.
- Weight loss.
- Deterioration of the coat—becomes lifeless and dehydrated.
- Mouth ulcers.
- Weakness, lethargy, disinclination to exercise.
- Change in character. Might become more affectionate, but usually becomes moody and prefers to hide away. Might even dig a hole and sit in the cold and rain.

For more details see chapter 15, 'Kidneys and bladder'.

Oral disease

Warning signs could include:
- Drooling saliva.
- Reluctance to eat or pain when eating. The cat might seem interested, walk up to the food bowl, but then walk away again.
- Bad breath.
- Weight loss.

To check the teeth, lift the side of your cat's lip back to expose one side of the mouth. It is not necessary to open the mouth. Look especially at the gum/tooth margin for evidence of redness, discharge, ulceration or build up of a tartar deposit.

For more details see chapter 10, 'Teeth and mouth'.

Arthritis

The signs of arthritis are usually most obvious early in the morning, when the cat arises from a long rest or during damp, changeable weather. Warning signs could include:

- Wasting of the pelvic muscles.
- Reluctance to get up from rest or sit down again.
- Stiff, stilted gait.
- Difficulty or inability to jump up. You might, for example, note that the cat stops using a favoured chair and prefers to lie on the floor.
- Disinclination to groom, especially around the base of the tail.

For more details see chapter 17, 'Bones and joints'.

Heart disease

When the heart is diseased, all the organs are affected to some extent, so the signs can be confusing. Fortunately, heart disease is not common in cats. Vets find it difficult to evaluate the cat's heart effectively because it beats rapidly and is very small. Warning signs could include:

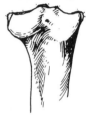

Arthritic changes within the knee joint. Some surfaces wear. Bony spurs and prominences can develop

- Decreased exercise tolerance. Cat becomes reluctant to move about, or moves only short distances before lying down. In some cases the cat appears to have difficulty getting comfortable.
- Cough—especially on awakening or starting to move around.
- Fluid retention in chest or abdomen. If the chest is affected the cat could have short, laboured breaths and perhaps a cough. If the abdomen is affected it will swell with fluid to give a pot-bellied appearance.
- Pallor of gums.
- Lethargy, depression, dullness.

In some cases, clots (thrombus) form in a major blood vessel. In these cases, signs could include:
- Cold leg. No detectable pulse.
- Pain in affected leg or legs (could be both hind-limbs).
- Loss of function of affected leg(s).

For more details see chapter 16, 'Heart and lungs'.

HOW TO TELL IF YOUR CAT IS DEAD

- Breathing stops. Look for any movement of the chest or abdomen. You could hold a mirror next to the nose. Breathing will cause fogging of the glass.

- Heart stops. Check the femoral artery, which runs inside the cat's thigh. Or feel for the heart itself. It is on the left side, just behind and above the point of the elbow.
- Eyes. Reflexes go. The cat's eyes are open after death. Gently touch the eyeball with your finger. If the cat is dead there will be no reflex blink. The eye feels soft. Compare it with the tone of your own eyeball. The pupil of a dead cat is wide open.
- *Rigor mortis:* 15–30 minutes after death the cat's muscles begin to stiffen and the cat eventually becomes rigid. This rigor wears off to some degree several hours later.

Touch the cornea. After death there is no reflex blink

A DEATH IN THE FAMILY

Losing a pet is always difficult. It can be devastating. Your cat is special, unique. As its life draws to a close you will need to adjust to your impending loss and then find the best way to deal with the trauma. You might or might not get much time to face up to your cat's death. Knowing a little about euthanasia and grief might help you to cope better.

Euthanasia

The time might come when you are asked to consider having your cat's life ended. If you are fortunate, this will be at the end of a long life. However, it is sometimes necessary after an accident or an illness. You will be forced to weigh up the rights and wrongs of opting for surgical and medical efforts or to let go.

Euthanasia means 'easy and gentle death'. It is generally performed by a veterinarian, who gives an anaesthetic in a large overdose. Usually it takes only a few seconds. The cat literally goes to sleep, then all life ceases. Vets try to find the gentlest, least traumatic way possible for each individual patient. This might mean giving a sedative first, but it is not often necessary. Usually the cat has no knowledge of what is happening and will just relax and lose consciousness as the anaesthetic works.

Most owners wait a little too long before making the decision to have their pet 'put to sleep'. This is understandable; indeed, it is almost inevitable as there is always some hope, and you need to be absolutely certain about this irreversible decision. For your cat's sake, try to base it on what is best for the cat. Your choice is not likely to be easier in a week or a month's time. If euthanasia is clearly your best option, you owe it to your pet to somehow find the courage to make and stand by that decision.

If you need advice or help, talk to a friend who knows you and your cat; preferably someone who has been through such an experience. Your vet might be of great assistance at this time. If you are fortunate to have a good relationship with your vet, you might be able to tap into the experiences of hundreds of their clients as seen through their eyes. It might not be a decision you can make easily on your own, and can be a very painful dilemma. Make it in the best interests of your cat. Involve all members of your family if you can.

You will usually be given the option of staying with your cat or leaving the vet and nurse to perform the task alone. It can be incredibly difficult to stay, and it is an individual choice. Quite often one or two members of a family will stay while the others prefer to say goodbye and to leave. The vet will not judge you by that choice, nor by how you react at the time. Do not be embarrassed by tears or deep emotion. To us it is wonderful to see how much the cat has been loved, and we try to remain professional in ensuring that its death is as gentle as possible.

Grief

Grief is a normal reaction to loss. Whatever the reason your pet has died and by whatever means, you will feel a series of emotions, depending on your personality and the bonds you had. The more your cat meant to you, the more keenly you are likely to feel its loss. For many the impact of a pet's death is far greater than expected. Children in particular can be devastated, especially if the cat was the first thing they have truly loved and lost.

A very common remark from friends is: 'It's only a cat—you'll get over it'. Such comments are well meant but often result in you hiding or denying your feelings. We do not cope well with death in

Western society. Pet owners can be embarrassed, even ashamed, to admit how hard they feel the loss. Yet our cat can be just as important to us as other members of our family. Sadly, for many, the loss of their cat cuts deeper than any other. Perhaps the cat's trust in and dependence on you makes you feel that somehow you have let it down.

Several stages in the grieving process are recognised. It takes time to work through them. If you fight them off or deny them it could take years to come to terms with a death.

1 Shock.
2 Denial.
3 Guilt.
4 Anger.
5 Sadness.
6 Helplessness, depression.
7 Acceptance.

If you loved your cat you will feel dreadful for a while. It is natural to look for someone to blame—perhaps the vet, perhaps yourself. If you need to cry or to pound the wall, do so. Vent your feelings if you are able to. Release your safety valve. Frequently, we feel unable to do so. Perhaps we are afraid of being thought weak or of overreacting to the loss of 'just an animal'. However, if you can do it, the healing process will be accelerated, allowing you to come to terms with your loss.

Your sadness is a measure of your care. Unfortunately cats have a much shorter life span than our own. If you were forced to make the decision to choose euthanasia, be comforted in the knowledge that such a decision, made with love and compassion, was a final gift and one of peace, and this should help you to cope with your grief.

Index